When Life's a Drag

Women, Smoking and Disadvantage

Hilary Graham

WITHDRAWN
FROM
STOCK

Department of Health

London: HMSO

ISBN 0 11 321625 4

Contents

List of Figures

List of Tables

Acknowledgements

The study that forms the main focus of the book drew on the help of a number of agencies and individuals. I am grateful to the Department of Health for funding the study and to Dr Liza Catan and Ann Kauder for their support and encouragement. I would like to record my thanks to senior staff at the University Hospital, Nottingham and the Maternity Hospital, Coventry who provided essential help with the survey, and particularly Professor Malcolm Symonds and Dr Pamela Gillies, Mrs S Myhill and Mrs I G Sealy. I also wish to thank Social Community Planning Research and Galan Research and Consultancy, who conducted the interviews and data-analysis. Special thanks go to Sonia Conmy who typed and retyped her way through the manuscript. My greatest thanks goes to the mothers who shared their experiences. It is their time and their help which resourced the research on which this book is based. I would also like to thank Nicholas Ward for giving his permission for reproduction of Figures 1.1, 1.2, 1.3, 2.3, and 3.1

The views expressed in the course of the book are those of the author alone.

Hilary Graham
University of Warwick
July 1993

Introduction

Cigarette smoking is the dominant form of tobacco use in Britain. A small proportion of male smokers smoke a pipe or cigar; among female smokers, cigarette smoking is almost universal.

Cigarette smoking has been increasingly implicated as a cause of ill-health and premature death [1, 2]. For those who smoke cigarettes, 'giving up is the single most important step they could take to improve their health' [3]. Smoking also represents a significant risk to the health of others. Passive smoking imposes a particular burden on the health of children, before and after birth [4].

Increasing public awareness of the health risks of smoking has resulted in a sharp decline in smoking prevalence in Britain, as in other developed countries [5]. In Britain, smoking prevalence among men began to fall from the 1960s and accelerated through the 1970s and early 1980s. Smoking prevalence among women did not start to fall until the 1970s, and the decline, although sustained, has been a gradual one [6, 7].

It is the slow rate of decline in smoking prevalence that the government is seeking to tackle by setting ambitious targets for the reduction of cigarette smoking. The target for England is 'to reduce the prevalence of cigarette smoking to no more than 20% by the year 2000 in both men and women' [8]. Alongside this national target, the government has laid down targets for smoking cessation in pregnancy. *The Health of the Nation* states that, 'in addition to the overall reduction in prevalence, at least a third of women smoking (are) to stop smoking by the start of their pregnancy by the year 2000' [8].

These government targets represent a major challenge for those involved in promoting the nation's health. Smoking prevalence among women in England would need to fall by over 30% between 1990 and 2000 for the overall target to be achieved. It has taken two decades, not one, to achieve a reduction of this magnitude [7]. Rates of smoking cessation for early pregnancy are also currently well below the rates sought by the government for the year 2000 [9–11].

The scale of the challenge represented by *The Health of the Nation* is underlined when the targets are set against the changing social profile of women's smoking in Britain. Women's smoking in Britain, like cigarette smoking among men, is associated with social and economic disadvantage. Thus, women who left school at the minimum leaving age and who are unemployed are more likely to smoke than women who stayed on at school and who are in paid work. Women in council housing are more likely to smoke than women in owner-occupied housing. Lone mothers are more likely to smoke than mothers bringing up their children with a male partner [7,12–15].

The links between smoking and disadvantage emerge most clearly in the increasingly pronounced socio-economic differences in women's smoking. While prevalence rates have fallen among women in all socio-economic groups since the 1970s, the rate of decline has been most marked among women in non-manual households [6, 7]. As a result, a clear class gradient has emerged in women's smoking. The proportion of cigarette smokers in the lowest socio-economic group is now twice that found among women in the highest socio-economic group [7]. Among expectant mothers, a key target group for smoking cessation programmes, the class differences are sharper still. Recent surveys suggest that smoking prevalence before pregnancy is three times higher among women in social class V than among women in social class I. Further, while smoking prevalence rates are significantly higher, smoking cessation rates are significantly lower: it is women on the higher rungs of the class ladder who are most likely to give up smoking in pregnancy [11].

In the past, ignorance of the harmful effects of cigarette smoking was a major factor in sustaining high levels of smoking [16]. Today, studies point to a more complex relationship between knowledge and behaviour. Young adolescents have very negative attitudes to smoking, yet by the time they are 15 one in five is a regular smoker [17]. Among adults, the majority of smokers, like the majority of non-smokers, recognise both the general and the specific health risks of smoking [13, 16, 18]. In fact, it appears that smokers are more aware than non-smokers of the associations between smoking and general ill-health and between smoking and specific conditions, such as heart disease and bronchitis [13]. Such evidence suggests that increasing and refining health knowledge is unlikely to achieve the scale of reduction in smoking prevalence sought by the government. It points, instead, to the need to understand more about the mechanisms that sustain cigarette smoking in circumstances of disadvantage and in the face of knowledge of its harmful effects.

The book focuses on the connections between women's smoking and disadvantage. Part I reviews the evidence on the changing patterns of women's smoking, pointing to the way in which current trends in smoking prevalence are combining to make White working class women an increasingly important group within Britain's smoking population. The second part of the book reports on a study designed to shed light on the connections between the smoking behaviour of White working class women and the circumstances of their daily lives. Based on interviews with 905 mothers in manual households, the survey found higher rates of smoking prevalence and higher levels of cigarette consumption among mothers who carried additional caring responsibilities and who lived in more disadvantaged circumstances. The study suggests that additional caring responsibilities and more restricted access to material resources work against smoking cessation and work to maintain higher levels of both prevalence and consumption. Through their answers, the mothers graphically illustrate how cigarette smoking is part of the way in which women caring in circumstances of disadvantage cope 'when life's a drag'.

The chapters rely primarily on quantitative data to explore the connections between women's smoking and their everyday lives. However, the book also includes accounts that women have given of the meaning and significance they attach to smoking. The personal statements are woven between the text and the tables as a separate but linked commentary on how mothers view their smoking habit.

Part I
Trends in Women's Smoking in Britain

Chapter 1

Women's smoking:
an early twentieth century history

1.1   Introduction

The chapter provides a brief history of women's smoking in Britain from 1900 to 1970. The section below describes the beginnings of women's smoking in the 1920s and 1930s, while section 1.3 tracks the rapid rise and more gradual decline of the female smoker since the 1940s.

It should be noted that smoking data derive primarily from surveys of self-reported behaviour. A comparison of these data with information based on the sales of tobacco products and on tobacco tax revenues suggests that surveys provide an underestimate of both prevalence and consumption [1–5]. In addition to non-response, some smokers mask the fact and the scale of their smoking habit. While some studies suggest that the increasing medical and social disapproval of smoking has increased the scale of under-reporting, other surveys indicate relatively small changes in the reliability of self-estimated smoking behaviour [1, 2]. In the sections that follow, figures and tables adjusted to take account of under-reporting are marked 'sales adjusted'. No adjustments, however, are applied to the major source of smoking data, the General Household Survey, or to the survey which provides the focus of Part II of the book.

1.2   The beginnings of women's smoking: 1900 to 1940

Tobacco consumption among women is a recent phenomenon. During the nineteenth century, tobacco consumption was the preserve of men and it was considered improper for women and children to use tobacco [6]. At that time, pipes, cigars and snuff, along with tobacco chewing, were the dominant forms of tobacco use. The smoking of manufactured cigarettes was a minority habit. In 1890, manufactured cigarettes made up less than 2% of the total annual sales of tobacco products in the UK: 98% of the market was accounted for by tobacco for pipes, cigars, chewing and snuff [3].

The first factory making cigarettes was established in London in 1856. However, it was not until the late 1880s that the sale of manufactured cigarettes began to rise. From 1895, sales increased rapidly and by 1919 cigarettes accounted for more sales by weight than all other tobacco products combined. In that year, 71,300 tonnes of tobacco products were sold in the UK, with manufactured cigarettes accounting for 51% of this total [3].

Women's smoking in Britain is linked to the rise of manufactured cigarettes as the dominant form of tobacco use. However, in the early decades of the twentieth century, it was changes in tobacco use among men that fuelled the rapid increase in the sale and consumption of cigarettes [3]. The social prohibition on women's smoking was still strong during this period, both here and in the US [7]. One study describes how, in 1904, a policeman arrested a woman for smoking a cigarette in New York, with the admonition, 'you can't do that in Fifth Avenue' [8].

The 1914–1918 war is credited with removing some of the censure attached to women's smoking [7]. However, it was not until 1921 that tobacco consumption among women in Britain reached recordable levels. In that year, women consumed 300 tonnes of tobacco products, all in the form of manufactured cigarettes. Men consumed 67,600 tonnes of tobacco products (manufactured cigarettes and other tobacco products) in the same year – over 200 times the consumption of women [3]. Through the 1920s and 1930s, women's tobacco consumption increased rapidly (Figure 1.1). The increase was confined to manufactured cigarettes: the traditional forms of tobacco use, like pipes and cigars, remained male forms of consumption, as they have done since.

There is little evidence on the social background of female smokers in the 1920s and 1930s. The limited information suggests that cigarette smoking was a symbol of emancipation and sexual equality, a fashion accessory for affluent, upwardly-mobile city-living women [7, 9]. As today, the media both reflected and reinforced images of appropriate behaviour for women. A 1930s study of the contemporary cinema found that heroes and heroines were portrayed as cigarette smokers, while the villains and the villainesses were non-smokers. Within its

Figure 1.1 Total annual consumption of tobacco products (thousands of tonnes manufactured weight) by men and women, 1905 to 1950, UK

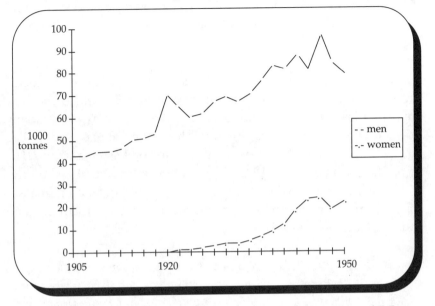

Source: derived from N Wald, S Kiryluk, S Darby, R Doll, M Pike and R Peto (1988) *UK Smoking Statistics*, Table 1.3.

sample of 40 films, 30% of heroines were smokers, compared with less than 3% of the villainesses. Among men, the proportions were 65% for heroes and 23% for villains [10]. Outside the movie-world, evidence on female tobacco consumption suggests that women's smoking was still very much a minority habit. It was also one that women tended to take up in adulthood rather than in adolescence. Among women aged 20 in 1939, only one in eight was a smoker [11].

1.3   Increasing prevalence: 1940 to 1970

Like the 1914–18 war, the 1939–45 war changed the position and lifestyles of women in Britain. It opened up new worlds, with women between the ages of 18 and 50 taking up paid and voluntary work in factories, shops, schools and hospitals, as well as in the armed forces. But wartime conditions also disrupted work and leisure habits, bringing rationing and material shortage, day and night-time air-raids and continuing anxieties about children and absent partners. Traditional leisure pursuits were restricted, with surveys of wartime Britain reporting how men and women were doing less leisure-time travelling, playing less sport and going out less to the cinema and to see friends. There were two exceptions to this pattern of doing less:

smoking and drinking [12]. Smoking prevalence among women rose sharply, a rise linked to a rapid fall in the age of female smokers. By 1945, one in three women aged 20 was a smoker. As with men, regular smoking had become firmly established as a habit acquired during adolescence and early adulthood [11].

The limited evidence suggests that the rapid change in women's smoking habits during the war years was linked both to the new opportunities and to the increasing restrictions on women's daily lives. Young women were entering the armed forces and public houses, where cigarette smoking was a major leisure pursuit. The accounts of women in the WAAF record the high value placed on cigarettes, with protests when their cigarette allocation failed to materialise and an appreciation of cigarettes given as part of the friendship and courtship process [13].

> The longer you can keep your man, the higher up you are in the competition. It's better if he's madly in love with you. He shouldn't be seen in public with other women. And telegrams, chocolates, cigarettes and really 'classy' evenings out all put you one step higher on the ladder.
>
> Woman in the WAAF, 1941 [i]

Women in and out of uniform were also increasingly seen in pubs, where cigarettes were part of the social exchange [14]. The comments below capture the observations of a publican and a female drinker on the increasing involvement of women in pub-life.

> Lots more (women) than before the war – I should say it's mainly because younger women are earning more money than before ... They usually behave quite well. I have nothing against it.
>
> Fulham publican, 1943 [ii]

> I don't see no harm in it – it's 'ard' to get stuff to take 'ome nowadays and pubs are more lively places for a body to go. Those who don't drink or smoke, there's something wrong with them; that's my honest opinion.
>
> Female smoker, 1943 [ii]

Studies suggest that cigarette smoking was also part of the way in which civilians coped with the restrictions and hardships of war, and the blitz in particular. Smoking was one of the habits done significantly more by those living in blitzed areas. In London, in common with other bombed cities and towns, outside leisure activities, like films and sport, gave way to private pursuits and to a communal shelter life [12]. Cigarette smoking was an activity routinely observed among women in air-raid shelters [14].

> *Many shelters, particularly those of the brick surface type, provide poor light and facilities for the staple leisure occupations of women, knitting or reading. Out of 16 women observed in a West London brick shelter, ... 50% of the women observed were doing nothing at all or just smoking, while in a brick shelter in the North where light was confined to a hurricane lamp, during 40 alarms observed during August–September, reading only occurred twice ... Women were too tired after an endless succession of alarms to have much enthusiasm for anything.*
>
> Observation in a London air-raid shelter, 1940 [iii]

> *In London during the heavy raids I found smoking a great help. My consumption has gone up over 100%. It started in September – during the blitz. I found smoking kept me from getting jittery*
>
> Woman in the blitz, 1941 [iv]

Figure 1.2   Cigarette smoking among women in 1949 by age, Britain

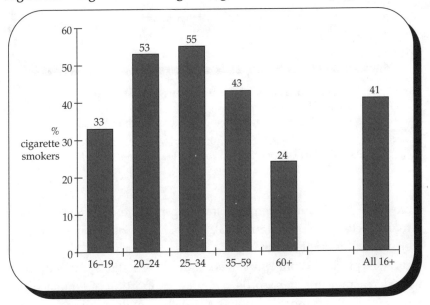

Note: Includes manufactured cigarettes only.

Source: derived from N Wald, S Kiryluk, S Darby, R Doll, M Pike and R Peto (1988) *UK Smoking Statistics*, Table 4.1.2.

The changes in the smoking habits of women persisted after the war, with sharp differences in the smoking habits of women under and over the age of 60. In 1949, over 50% of women between the ages of 20 and 34 were cigarette smokers (Figure 1.2). Most of the new female smokers, however, were light smokers. Until the mid-1950s, female smokers were smoking an average of less than 10 cigarettes a day [3].

Figure 1.3   Prevalence of cigarette smoking among men and women aged 16 and over, 1948 to 1990, Britain ʒ

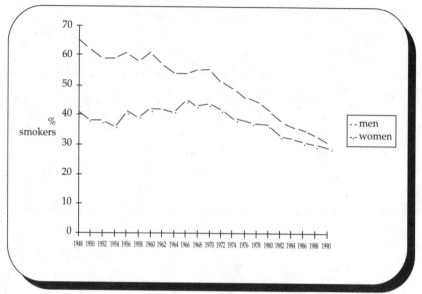

Note: 1.   Data up to 1972 include manufactured cigarettes only, sales-adjusted 1969–1985.
        2.   Data from 1972 include manufactured and hand-rolled cigarettes.
Source: derived from N Walk, S Kiryluk, S Darby, R Doll, M Pike and R Peto (1988) *UK Smoking Statistics*, Table 3.3 and *General Household Survey 1990*, Table 6.2. HMSO.

Across the next quarter century, smoking prevalence among women remained close to 40% (Figure 1.3). In 1949, 41% of women in Britain were cigarette smokers; in 1972, 41% of women were still smoking cigarettes [3, 15]. While prevalence rates were stable, consumption was increasing. In other words, a similar proportion of female smokers were smoking more cigarettes. In 1949, female smokers over the age of 16 consumed an average of 48 cigarettes a week, half the level of male cigarette consumption. By 1976, average consumption among women stood at 101 cigarettes a week, twice the level in 1949. Across this period, male consumption had also risen, but much less sharply. Between the late 1940s and the mid 1970s, average cigarette consumption among men had risen by 30% [3, 15].

It was not until the mid-1970s that women's smoking began to decline in popularity. The last two decades have seen a sustained decline both in smoking prevalence and in tobacco consumption among women. This decline has been associated with a rapid change in the gender composition of cigarette smokers in Britain. The changing gender profile of cigarette smoking is the focus of Chapter 2.

Notes

i. 'Nina Masel: confessions of a WAAF, 1941–3' in Calder A and Sheridan D (eds) (1984) *Speak for Yourself: A Mass Observation Anthology 1937–49*, p134.

ii. quoted in Sheridan D (ed) (1990) *War-time Women: A Mass Observation Anthology*, p197.

iii. ibid., p119.

iv. quoted in Harrison, T (1976) *Living Through the Blitz*, p312–3.

Chapter 2

Women's smoking:
a late twentieth century history

2.1 Introduction

For most of the century, cigarette smoking has had a clear male identity. In recent decades, however, surveys suggest that its gender profile is changing. In the 1990s, more women than men are taking up
smoking in the crucial adolescent years when smoking careers are
established and fewer women than men are giving up smoking in
later life. As a result, the prevalence rates of adult men and women
are converging. Today, almost as many women as men over the age of
16 are engaged in what has been identified as the single major pre-
ventable cause of illness and premature death in the UK.

The chapter begins by describing this rapid change in the gender distribution of cigarette smoking. It then turns to consider the patterns
of cigarette smoking in adolescence, the period in which Britain's
future smokers acquire their habit and the new gender profile in cigarette smoking is at its most pronounced.

2.2 The decline in women's smoking: 1970 to 1990

Smoking prevalence rates among women reached their peak in 1966,
when 45% of women were smokers [1]. However, surveys suggest
that prevalence rates among younger women continued to rise until
the early 1970s. In 1970, over half of women aged 16 to 19 were
recorded as cigarette smokers, with overall prevalence rates kept
below the 45% peak of 1966 only by the much lower prevalence rates
found among women aged 60 and over [1].

Since the 1970s, prevalence rates among women in the 16 to 59 age
band have fallen significantly [2]. However, the rate of decline has
been lower among women in the 16 to 19 and 20 to 24 age groups
than among women into the older age groups. Between 1972 and
1990, the prevalence rate among women aged 16 to 19 fell by 18%;
among women aged 50 to 59, it fell by 38% [2]. These contrasting

patterns of reduction in cigarette-smoking prevalence are summarised in Figure 2.1.

Figure 2.1   The decline in cigarette smoking prevalence among women by age: percentage reduction between 1972 and 1990, Britain

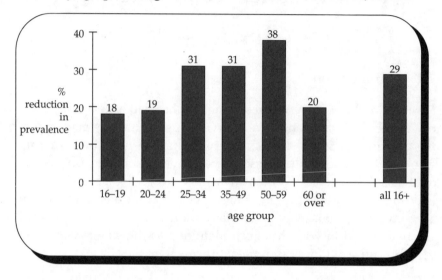

Note: Cigarette smoking includes manufactured and hand-rolled cigarettes.

Source: derived from OPCS (1992) *General Household Survey 1990*, Table 6.3. HMSO.

Over the last decade, the downward trend in smoking among women in the younger age groups has levelled off. From the late 1980s, there is evidence of an increase in smoking prevalence among women in the 16 to 19 and 20 to 24 age groups (Figure 2.2). In 1990, 32% of women aged 16 to 19 and 39% of women aged 20 to 24 reported that they smoked cigarettes [2].

2.3   The changing gender profile of cigarette smoking

In Britain in 1948, twice as many men as women were smokers: 82% of men and 41% of women were recorded as smoking some form of tobacco [1]. When cigarette smoking is considered separately, the gender difference narrows. Nonetheless, it is still pronounced, with one and a half times as many men as women in 1948 reporting that they smoked cigarettes [1].

Today, smoking prevalence for both men and women is significantly lower. The gender profile of smoking, too, has changed. In 1990, 38%

Figure 2.2   Prevalence of cigarette smoking among men & women aged 16 to 24, 1972 to 1990, Britain

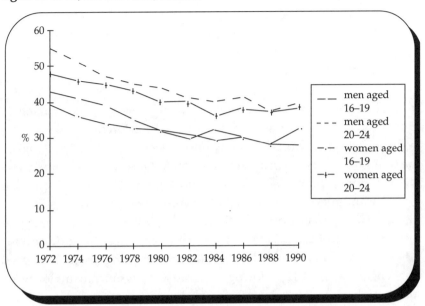

Note: Cigarette smoking includes manufactured and hand-rolled cigarettes.

Source: derived from OPCS (1992) *General Household Survey 1990*, Table 6.3.
HMSO.

of men and 31% of women were smokers (all tobacco products) [2]. Among cigarette smokers, the gender difference in prevalence has all but disappeared. In 1990, 31% of men and 29% of women were smoking cigarettes (manufactured and hand-rolled) (Figure 1.3).

The narrowing of the traditional gender difference in cigarette smoking is most pronounced among young people. Here, the gender balance has now been reversed. In 1990, the smoking prevalence rates among women aged 16 to 19 and 20 to 24 overtook those of men for the first time (Figure 2.2). It is not until men and women reach the age of 25 that the traditional gender profile begins to re-emerge. As the younger cohorts age, the smoking population is likely to become increasingly female.

Similar trends are evident in other developed countries. The sharp gender differences found in the 1940s, 1950s and 1960s in Australia, New Zealand, Canada, the US and Sweden have now disappeared. As in Britain, male and female smoking prevalence rates have converged [3–7]. In countries like Finland where men still make up the majority of cigarette smokers, the gender gap is closing [8].

The narrowing of the traditional gender difference in the prevalence of cigarette smoking in Britain reflects a number of trends. It reflects the fact that the proportion who have never smoked cigarettes has risen much more rapidly among men than among women [2]. The proportion of ex-cigarette smokers has also increased more rapidly among men than women [1, 2].

In interpreting these patterns of smoking among men and women, it must be remembered that they refer only to cigarette smoking. The exclusion of other forms of tobacco-use, like pipes and cigars, makes the trend towards equalisation in the smoking prevalence of men and women more pronounced than it would otherwise be. This is because a significant minority of men smoke pipes and cigars, the traditional nineteenth century forms of tobacco use, while female smoking is restricted almost exclusively to cigarette smoking. Including these other forms of tobacco use leaves women's smoking prevalence rates unchanged, at 29% [2]. However, because a significant minority of male smokers are not cigarette smokers, prevalence rates based on cigarette smokers underestimate smoking prevalence among men [9]. Including pipes and cigars raises the male smoking prevalence rate from the 31% recorded for cigarette smokers to 38% for all forms of tobacco [2].

Sociolog - Gender - not cigars

The exclusion of pipe and cigar smoking from the national estimates of smoking also has the effect of exaggerating gender differences in smoking cessation. Again, this is because of continuing gender differences in these traditional forms of tobacco use, with male but not female ex-cigarette smokers represented among the pipe and cigar-smoking population. If these secondary pipe and cigar smokers are categorised as continuing smokers (rather than as ex-smokers), then the cessation rate for men is substantially reduced and the excess of male over female cessation narrows considerably [2, 9–11]. For men, the exclusion of cigar and pipe smokers from the ranks of the ex-smokers reduces the overall cessation rate from 51% to 43%. The exclusion of pipe and cigar smokers from the population of female ex-smokers does not alter the smoking cessation rate. Of all the women in Britain who report they have smoked cigarettes, now or in the past, 39% are ex-smokers [2].

Comparisons of overall smoking prevalence and cessation among men and women based on trends in cigarette smoking thus need to be interpreted with caution. Nonetheless, it is clear that women make up an increasing proportion of the declining population of smokers in Britain and make up almost half of its cigarette smoking population.

The narrowing of gender differences in the prevalence of cigarette smoking is matched by a narrowing of gender differences in cigarette consumption. Average cigarette consumption is lower for women than for men, reflecting the fact that women have traditionally smoked fewer cigarettes than men. However, this traditional gender difference is narrowing. Average cigarette consumption among men started to fall in the early 1970s, when average consumption among

Figure 2.3 Weekly consumption of cigarettes per smoker among men and women aged 16 and over, 1950 to 1990, Britain

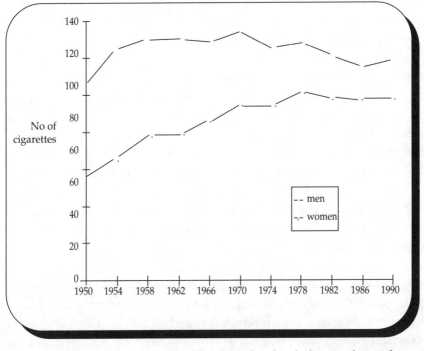

Notes: Data for 1950 to 1972 are sales-adjusted and include manufactured cigarettes only.

Source: derived from N Wald, S Kiryluk, S Darby, R Doll, M Pike and R Peto (1988) *UK Smoking Statistics*, Tables 4.10 & 4.10.2, and OPCS (1992) *General Household Survey 1990*, Table 6.7. HMSO.

women was still rising. Cigarette consumption among women smokers peaked in the late 1970s, before declining gradually. The survey evidence suggests that the decline in average consumption among women has now slowed to a crawl. As a result of these trends, consumption rates among men and women have been converging (Figure 2.3).

This convergence reflects other trends in women's smoking. Across the last two decades, female ex-smokers have been drawn disproportionately from the ranks of the light smokers. As a result, women smoking 20 or more cigarettes a day make up a larger proportion of the female smoking population than they did in the early 1970s. Among men, the proportion of heavy smokers in 1990 closely matches the proportion in 1970.

2.4   Gender differences in smoking among young people

Adult smoking habits are laid down in adolescence. Three-quarters of the adults who smoke today were smoking regularly by the time they were 18 [12]. It is the current patterns of smoking among young people that determine the future patterns of smoking in Britain.

Regular adult smoking has its origins in experimental teenage smoking. By the age of 16, seven in ten young people in Britain have tried smoking [13]. Studies suggest that the inhalation of cigarette smoke results in a pharmacological dependence on cigarettes, with dependence mediated through the effects of nicotine [14]. The effects of nicotine include the control of a person's psychological state, with smokers reporting that they experience smoking as a way of enhancing both mood and performance [15]. Surveys point to the early development of dependence on cigarettes among young people experimenting with smoking [16].

Through the 1980s, boys were more likely than girls to experiment with cigarettes. This gender difference has now been reversed. Today, experimenting is more common among girls [13]. The patterns of experimentation are reflected in the patterns of regular smoking among young people. Among young people, regular smoking is typically defined as smoking at least one cigarette a week. Findings from a range of studies confirm that regular smoking is more common among girls than boys in the 11 to 15 age group both in Britain and Northern Ireland [13, 17–20].

By the age of 15, one in four young women in England and Wales is a smoker. Among young women in Scotland, the proportion is higher. As Figure 2.4 indicates, 28% of Scotland's 15 year old women are regular smokers [13]. The patterns mapped out in Figure 2.4 are evident in other developed countries [3-7]. A mid-1980s survey of 15 year olds in Europe uncovered a higher prevalence rate among young women than young men in five of the ten European countries surveyed [21].

Figure 2.4   Proportion of regular smokers among 15 year olds, 1990, Britain

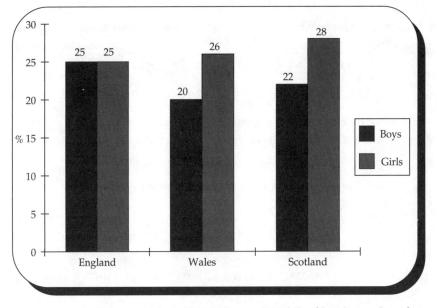

Source: derived from D Lader and J Matheson, (1991) *Smoking Among Secondary School Children in 1990*, Tables 3.16–3.18. HMSO.

As Figure 2.4 indicates, being a girl is now a major risk factor for starting smoking [22]. But the risks are not equally shared. Adolescent smoking is predominantly an activity of White girls: reported rates of smoking among young Asian and African-Caribbean women are low [23]. Having a parent and having siblings who smoke are both positively associated with adolescent smoking, factors which work to increase prevalence rates among young White women and depress rates among young Asian and African-Caribbean women [13, 20, 22–24]. The smoking attitudes and behaviour of friends have also been identified as significant factors in smoking initiation [18, 20, 24].

> *I wanted to learn. You practice on your own or with a friend. In back gardens or, you know, you pretend you're going for a walk, well away from the house.*

(Interviewer) When do you smoke now?

When I go out I smoke the most ... at college I tend to smoke a lot.

(Interviewer) Why do girls smoke, do you think?

Nearly all my friends smoke ... it's really unusual to find a girl that doesn't smoke. But it's not unusual to find a boy who doesn't smoke.

Psycholog

Young female smoker [i]

Studies have highlighted how female cigarette smoking is associated with other health-related behaviours. These include weight control, with smoking identified as a way of keeping slim [23, 25].

> *At school, girls pounce on fat girls. They laugh at them and fight them 'cause they're fat. They laugh at them and fight them 'cause they're too fat. With smoking my weight can be maintained. I will not get into fights.*
>
> *I guess I won't get married or find a good job or do something with my life 'cause I can't control my weight even with cigarettes.*
>
> *I don't snack as much when I smoke, so I keep my weight under control.*

Young women smokers [ii]

As among boys, cigarette smoking among young women is linked to alcohol consumption and illegal drug use, to early sexual experience and to social activities more generally [13, 20, 23, 26–28].

> *(Having a cigarette) makes me feel more in the mood to party. I feel quite comfortable as well with one ... If you're standing around it feels like you're doing something you know, because if you're standing like this you feel silly, so you have a cigarette, you know, it feels like you're doing something.*

Sociogical

Young woman aged 15 to 17 [iii]

Studies of young people also point to a link between cigarette smoking and social disadvantage. Smoking emerges as one element in a youth culture which underwrites adolescent identity in circumstances where other sources of self-esteem, including education and employment, are beyond reach [21, 23, 26, 28]. As a number of surveys have confirmed, young women and men who live in rented accommodation and in one-parent households are more likely to take up smoking [22–24, 29, 30]. Low self-esteem and low educational aspirations have also been identified as important predictors of smoking among school children [22–24, 29, 31]. School children who expect to stay on in full-time education are significantly less likely to be regular smokers than other pupils [20–22, 29]. A European study of smoking among young people underlined this strong relationship between smoking status and academic ambitions. It concluded that the probability of being a school-age smoker increases significantly when a student reports poor school achievement, dislikes school and has no plans for further education [21].

In exploring the links between cigarette smoking, low self-esteem and low expectations for the future, studies have pointed to the way in which cigarette smoking is experienced as a resource that can be drawn on in times of need [15, 32]. It is a resource that young smokers, and young female smokers in particular, identify as important in mood management. Cigarettes are identified as a way of relaxing and away of coping with difficult feelings, including insecurity, depression and anger [13, 20, 23, 24, 31].

> It helps to relax me. If I'm uptight … it helps me unwind.
> It relaxes me when I'm down.
>
> I had my first cigarette when I came to London (from Devon at 14). Partly, I wanted to try it; it was nothing to do with friends or anything, it just felt alright, it felt; you know, a way of sorting out the problems-type thing and then later on I got to know more people that did and it was, you know, more of a social thing.
>
> I smoke when I've had an argument with my Mum or Dad or I feel depressed.
>
> Sometimes it calms me down after I've just argued with my friends or parents.
>
> It's something to do when depressed. To get back at my parents. To be different.
>
> *Young female smokers [iv]*

There is evidence to suggest that cigarettes provide a particularly crucial resource for those facing life-events and experiences from which most children are protected. Young women confronting parental illness and death and those who are living with financial hardship and under the threat of eviction have described how cigarettes are a reliable friend in an uncertain and frightening world [33].

I think it [smoking] was just due to mom not being well, cos she's got cancer at the moment. So it's due ... I don't know, it's just sort of stress you know. You're in the house on your own and you ... I went through a sort of stage where I didn't want to see anyone so I was sort of on my own, and you can't really sit and read a book so you think what the heck can I do and instead of twiddling your thumbs. I don't know what made me do it. I just went round the corner, bought a packet of cigarettes and smoked a cigarette.

Young female smoker [v]

I live from day to day not knowing if the lights would be turned off, 'phone disconnected, or we'd have food to eat. I know it just wastes money when I buy cigarettes, but I don't drink or use drugs. Smoking is the only thing I do for myself. I don't have money to go to the movies or skating rinks like other kids.

I don't think I can ever stop smoking 'cause cigarettes have been there for me. Through thick and thin, they have been there for me.

I lived on the streets for 'bout nine months. My mother threw me out of the house. I didn't own nothing but the clothes on my back and a pack of cigarettes, but they were there for me and I consider them the only friend I can count on.

Young female smokers [vi]

2.5 Summary

In the early decades of the century, very few women smoked cigarettes. In the closing decades of the century, more young women than young men are smoking cigarettes regularly. These trends point to a feminisation of cigarette smoking, a process in which the decline in smoking prevalence is associated with a change in its gender distribution. This process of feminisation is part of wider changes in the patterns of cigarette smoking in Britain. These changes are examined in chapter 3.

Notes

i. woman aged 15–17 quoted in Oakley, A., Brannan, J. and Dodd, K. (1992) 'Young people, gender and smoking in the United Kingdom', *Health Promotion International*, 7, 2: 81–2.

ii. women aged 16–18 quoted in Lawson, E. (1993) *The Role of Smoking in the Lives of Low-income Pregnant Adolescents*, University of Kentucky, p10–11.

iii. woman aged 15–17, in Oakley, op.cit, p78.

iv.   ibid, p83–4.

v.   ibid, p84.

iv.   Lawson, op.cit, p12–13.

Chapter 3

Current patterns of women's smoking

3.1 Introduction

The decline in smoking prevalence in Britain and Northern Ireland has not only been associated with a rapid shift in its gender distribution. It has been linked, too, with a shift in the class base of cigarette smoking. Men and women in manual households make up an increasing proportion of the UK's declining smoking population. In other developed countries, widening class differences in women's smoking are linked to sharp ethnic differences, with women from minority ethnic groups more likely to report themselves as smokers than women from majority ethnic groups. In Britain, however, cigarette smoking has retained its strong ethnic identity, as a habit of White women. Surveys also point to an association between smoking and caring, with higher prevalence rates found among women looking after children and adults who need help with everyday health tasks.

The chapter explores the changes and continuities in women's smoking in Britain. The three sections below examine the ethnic identity and socio-economic background of Britain's female smokers, while the final section reviews the evidence linking smoking and caring. As noted in chapter 1, the surveys which track these links rely on self-reported smoking behaviour.

3.2 Ethnic identity

There is little information on the ethnic identity of Britain's female smokers. The limited evidence suggests that cigarette smoking among women is a White pattern of behaviour. Surveys in the 1970s relied on place of birth as an indicator of ethnic identity. They uncovered significantly higher smoking prevalence rates among White than Black women [1, 2]. In the mid-1970s, over 40% of women born in the UK reported themselves to be a smoker. Among women born in the

Caribbean, the smoking prevalence rate was 22% and among women born in South Asia, it was 13% [1]. Heavy smoking has a particularly clear ethnic identity, as a habit practiced among women born in the UK and Ireland.

Recent surveys confirm these sharp ethnic differences in women's smoking [3, 4]. The findings of a mid-1980s survey are described in Table 3.1 [5, 6]. Based on interviewer-defined ethnic identity, it suggests that one in three White women was a cigarette smoker. The proportion among African-Caribbean women was one in five (22%). Among Asian women, it was one in twenty (5%). Similar patterns have been uncovered among young women and among expectant mothers, with White women reporting significantly higher smoking prevalence rates than African-Caribbean and Asian women [7,8].

Table 3.1: **Smoking among men and women by interviewer-assessed ethic group, 1985, Britain**

Ascribed Ethnic Group	Smokers %	
	Men	Women
Indian	49	5
Black	40	22
Other non-White	43	32
White	37	36

Source: Cox, B.D. (ed) (1987) *Health and Lifestyle Survey,* unpublished data.

The ethnic differences in self-reported smoking behaviour are likely to reflect the cluster of religious and cultural influences that shape ideas of what is appropriate behaviour for women [9, 10]. For example, according to the Sikh code of conduct, Sikhs are asked to refrain from drinking alcohol and smoking cigarettes. A survey of young Sikh women in the Midlands found that the majority of young second generation Sikh women accepted and respected these traditional values. Female cigarette smoking was regarded as morally reprehensible as well as unhealthy [9].

While prevalence rates among Black women are low, it is important to recognise that smoking behaviour is not a fixed cultural trait. There is some evidence, for example, of increasing smoking prevalence among young middle class African-Caribbean women [7]. The international evidence on cigarette smoking underlines how quickly ethnic and gender identities can change. This evidence suggests that, unlike in Britain, smoking status in developed countries is often strongly linked to minority ethnic status and to the social and economic disadvantages associated with it. For example, in the US the smoking prevalence rate is higher among the Black than the White population, for both women and men. In New Zealand, Maori women have significantly higher smoking prevalence rates than Pakeha (White) women [11–14].

3.3 Socio-economic background

Information on the socio-economic background of Britain's smokers was not routinely collected until the 1950s. From 1958, the surveys conducted under the auspices of the Tobacco Advisory Council (TAC) mapped out the socio-economic profile of women's smoking, using the Registrar General's classification of social class [15]. Since 1972, the General Household Survey (GHS) has provided information on smoking status by socio-economic group [16]. While the measures used in the TAC surveys and the GHS are not identical, there is a reasonable degree of correspondence between them. Both surveys also follow a similar set of procedures to determine the social class/socio-economic group of women. Men earn their class and socio-economic position directly, on the basis of their own occupation; however, women's social position is mediated by their marital status. Single women (including previously married women) are classified by their own occupation. Married and cohabiting women who are living with their husband/male partner are ascribed a socio-economic position on the basis of his occupation. This approach is also the one used in one-off surveys, including the Health and Lifestyle Survey and the rich seam of studies charting the patterns of women's smoking in pregnancy [5, 17–19]. It is also the approach adopted in the survey of working class mothers, which forms the focus of Part II of the book.

The evidence from these continuous and one-off surveys points to a rapid change in the socio-economic profile of women's smoking in Britain. In the 1920s and 1930s, female smoking was associated with affluence and upward social mobility. In the 1940s, smoking prevalence rates were at their highest among women in the highest income group [15]. Fifty years on, cigarette smoking has lost its upper class associations. Instead, it is linked to low socio-economic status and to social disadvantage.

The change in the socio-economic profile of women's smoking is captured in Figures 3.1 and 3.2. Figure 3.1 describes the social class distribution of women's smoking in 1958. By the late 1950s, cigarette smoking had lost its association with high socio-economic status and displayed a uniform class distribution. Four in ten women in social class I to V reported that they smoked cigarettes. Among women in households where the head of household had been unemployed for more than two months, smoking prevalence rates were significantly lower. Among women in this group, 23% were smokers (Figure 3.1).

Figure 3.1   Prevalence of cigarette smoking among women by social class, 1958, Britain

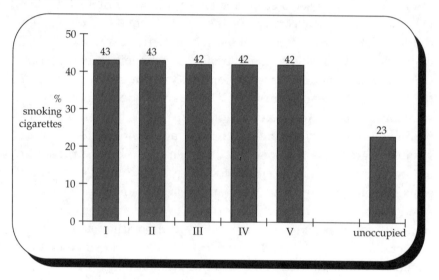

Notes: 1. Married women are classified on the basis of their husband's occupation.
2. Those who are retired and who have been unemployed for less than two months are classified according to their previous occupation.
3. Those who have been unemployed for more than two months are classified as unoccupied.

Source: derived from N Wald, S Kiryluk, S Darby, R Doll, M Pike and R Peto (1988) *UK Smoking Statistics*, Table 5.5.

Today, there is a sharp socio-economic gradient in both men's and women's smoking. In 1990, the proportion of smokers among women in unskilled manual households was twice as high as that found among women in professional households (Figure 3.2). Among men, too, there is a two-fold difference in smoking prevalence between the highest and lowest socio-economic groups.

2

Figure 3.2 Prevalence of cigarette smoking among women by socio-economic group, Britain, 1990

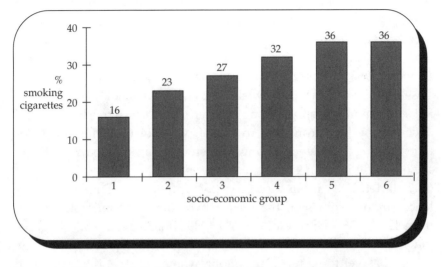

The socio-economic categories represented in Figure 3.2 are based on the current or last occupation of the head of household. Unlike the class groupings used in Figure 3.1, they therefore include married and cohabiting women with partners who are unemployed and single women who are unemployed. Looking at these groups of women separately suggests that unemployment has lost its association with low smoking prevalence. The evidence suggests that, in contrast to the 1950s, unemployment is associated with high smoking prevalence. Women living with unemployed partners are more likely to smoke than women whose partners are in paid work [20, 21]. Thus, for example, in one survey based in London, Edinburgh and Glasgow, over half the households had no-one in employment. The proportion of women who smoked was 70% [22]. National and local surveys suggest, too, that women who are unemployed are significantly more likely to be smokers than women in part-time or full-time work. In the General Household Survey, for example, the smoking prevalence among women in paid work is 31%; among women who are not in employment, 53% are cigarette smokers [16].

The emergence of a class gradient in cigarette smoking reflects the fact that men and women in higher socio-economic groups have turned away from smoking earlier and more quickly than those in manual groups. Smoking prevalence started to fall among women in social class I and II in the early 1960s, at a time when smoking prevalence rates among women in social class IV and V were still rising. Between 1958 and 1972, smoking prevalence among women in social class I fell by a quarter. Between 1972 and 1990, smoking prevalence fell even more sharply among women in professional households, declining by half, from 36% to 16%. It was not until the mid-1970s that smoking prevalence among women in semi-skilled and unskilled socio-economic groups began a sustained decline. The decline has not only started later: it has also been less pronounced. Smoking prevalence among women in the lowest two socio-economic groups fell from 42% to 36% between 1972 and 1990 [16]. As Figure 3.3 suggests, the rate of decline which has occurred in higher socio-economic groups has yet to be repeated among women on the lower rungs of the class ladder.

Figure 3.3 Prevalence of cigarette smoking among women in selected socio-economic groups, 1972 to 1990, Britain

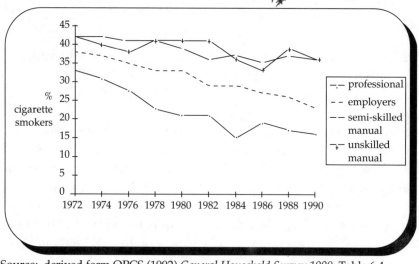

Source: derived form OPCS (1992) *General Household Survey 1990*, Table 6.4. HMSO.

Underlying the more rapid fall in the popularity of cigarette smoking among women and men in higher socio-economic groups are differences in the two factors that determine smoking prevalence: smoking initiation and smoking cessation. Firstly, the proportion of women who have never smoked has increased more rapidly among adults in non-manual households. Today, over 60% of women in professional households have never or have only occasionally smoked cigarettes: the proportion among women in unskilled manual households is 45% [16]. Secondly, a higher proportion of women in non-manual households have given up smoking. The ratio of smokers to ex-smokers among women in unskilled manual households is significantly lower than among women in professional households. For every hundred women who are current smokers in unskilled manual households, there are 53 ex-smokers; for every hundred women who are current smokers in professional households, there are 138 ex-smokers [16].

As the patterns mapped out in Figure 3.3 record, the decline in smoking prevalence has been associated with a rapid shift in its class profile. Similar trends are evident in other developed countries including the US, Canada and New Zealand [23–25]. As in Britain, a decline in smoking prevalence in these countries has been associated with both a narrowing of gender differences and a widening of class differences.

3.4 Socio-economic circumstances and smoking in pregnancy

The link between socio-economic status and smoking status is underlined in surveys of expectant mothers. Studies consistently report that high social class is linked to low smoking rates before pregnancy and high rates of smoking cessation during pregnancy [17–19]. Thus, in a recent UK survey, 17% of the expectant mothers with partners whose occupation fell into social class I were smokers before pregnancy compared with 47% of those living with partners in social class V (Table 3.2). Half the smokers in social class I gave up smoking in pregnancy compared with less than one in five women in social class V [19].

It is not only the traditional measures of socio-economic status that point to an association between disadvantage and smoking among pregnant women. Studies have uncovered an association between

Table 3.2: Smoking prevalence and smoking cessation among expectant mother by social class, 1990, UK

Social Class	% of mothers who smoked		% of mothers who gave up smoking during pregnancy
	before pregnancy	during pregnancy	
I	17	8	50
II	23	13	41
IIINM	26	16	41
IIIM	40	29	37
IV	45	34	24
V	47	39	17
No partner	62	53	16

Note: Social class is defined by current or last occupation of husband/male partner. Those without a male partner are classified separately.

Source: A White, S Freeth & M O'Brien (1992) *Infant Feeding 1990*, Table 2.11. HMSO.

smoking in pregnancy and benefit status, housing tenure and car ownership. Expectant mothers dependent on means-tested benefits, living in rented accommodation and without a car have higher prevalence rates than mothers in more advantaged circumstances [26]. Smoking in pregnancy is also known to be related to marital status, with lone expectant mothers reporting significantly higher smoking prevalence rates and significantly lower smoking cessation rates than married and cohabiting mothers [17–19]. As Table 3.2 suggests, lone mothers have a prevalence rate (62%) which exceeds that found among mothers living with men whose current or last occupation was an unskilled manual one (47%). Lone mothers also have the lowest reported rate of smoking cessation in pregnancy: only one in six (16%) of the lone mothers who were current smokers before pregnancy gave up smoking during pregnancy.

Age and educational background are also strongly correlated with smoking status in pregnancy. The highest prevalence rates are found among expectant mothers under the age of 20 and among women who left school at the minimum leaving age and with no educational qualifications. For example, studies point to smoking prevalence rates of between 40% and 60% among mothers under the age of 20 [17, 21, 27]. Smoking in pregnancy is also strongly associated with partner's smoking status [17, 28–29].

Marital status, mother's age and educational background, like the smoking status of her partner, are not independent of socio-economic position. Each of these measures is related to a woman's past and present socio-economic circumstances. The measures identify groups who have experienced, and continue to experience, multiple disadvantage. For example, lone mothers, young mothers and mothers without educational qualifications find their opportunities in the housing market and the labour market restricted. As a result, they are over-represented among households in rented housing and in temporary accommodation provided for homeless families, among households without an adult in employment and among households dependent on means-tested benefits [27, 30, 31]. Women with partners who smoke are similarly over-represented among those in poorer socio-economic circumstances [16].

Echoing themes identified in the smoking behaviour of young women, cigarette smoking has been identified as a resource which helps expectant mothers cope with difficult feelings and disadvantaged circumstances. Cigarette smoking provides a way of enhancing and controlling mood. Pregnant women report that they smoke to relax and calm their nerves, because of boredom and because they enjoy it [2, 26, 32–34]. In one recent study of expectant mothers, this cluster of reasons was given by more than half the mothers interviewed. Those who gave boredom as their main reason were significantly more likely to be younger mothers (aged 14 to 20), to be single and to have partners who were unemployed or with manual jobs. As the study concludes, 'it is perhaps not surprising that young mothers-to-be should cite boredom as their main reason for smoking' [34].

> If I'm moping or anything, I just have a fag. I think it's all in the mind really, you know like it calms you down, just in your mind ... I always have a cigarette with a cup of tea. I enjoy smoking.
>
> > Mother in low income household [i]

> I couldn't stop. I just couldn't. It keeps me calm. It's me one relaxation is smoking.

> They say it can be born dead if you smoke. I've cut down and I'm down to 10 a day. If I cut down any more I take it out on him (her son), which isn't fair on him. So it's one bairn or the other.
>
> > Expectant mothers [ii]

Expectant mothers have also described how smoking is linked to social and material stress, including marital breakdown and financial hardship. Their accounts suggest that having and smoking cigarettes provides them with a way of keeping going when they have little going for them [2, 26, 32–33, 35]. The links between cigarette smoking and the circumstances of mothers' everyday lives are explored further in the next section.

> *I was going to go on valium, but in the end I thought, no, don't, and coped, I coped without it. I was afraid that if I started anything like that, I wouldn't be able to give it up or get off it, so I went to cigarettes, and that was something I couldn't give up ... When I'm alright I don't smoke, but when I'm under stress, I do.*
>
> *(Interviewer) How much are you smoking now?*
>
> *Twenty now. I'm cutting them down, but I smoke because everything I have ever wanted has been ruined. I haven't got anything else left now.*
>
> > *Pregnant lone mother with a two-year old daughter, living in a women's refuge having left a violent marriage [iii]*

> *I feel like smoking is the only thing I've got for myself at the moment ... I don't go out. Sometimes I wish I hadn't had the children. When I gave up I was a very nervous person. I started again when my marriage broke up ... I was going through a lot of problems. If I'm depressed, I smoke about 40 a day ... Eventually I'd like to give up but with the divorce and everything I don't think I can at the moment. It's all I've got for myself.*
>
> > *Mother in low-income household [iv]*

3.5 Smoking and caring

In the early decades of the century, smoking was a habit established among women who were breaking with the social conventions which tied women to the home. The evidence from surveys today suggests that prevalence rates are higher among women in traditional caring roles.

Surveys conducted during the 1970s and 1980s pointed to a high smoking prevalence among nurses [36, 37]. More recent research suggests that the class backgrounds of nurses tends to be different from other professional groups of women, like teachers for example, in ways that account for at least some of the differences in their smoking behaviour [38, 39]. In other words, occupational differences in smoking prevalence are established prior to and not as a result of training and work experience. However, some groups of nurses appear to have particularly high rates, including psychiatric nurses and nursing auxiliaries [38, 40]. In one small-scale study of the employment influences on women's smoking, psychiatric nurses had a smoking prevalence rate twice that found among other groups of nurses [40].

Turning from women's paid caring roles to their unpaid caring responsibilities, social surveys provide further evidence of an association between caring and smoking. Among women in the 16 to 34 age group, those with dependent children are more likely to smoke than those without dependent children. Among married and cohabiting women aged 25 to 34, women with children have a prevalence rate of 33%; among women without children, the prevalence rate is 23% [16]. In the 16 to 24 age group, smoking prevalence among women with dependent children is over 40% (Figure 3.4). These differences reflect, at least in part, the different socio-economic circumstances of young women with and without children, with young mothers clustered among those in poorer circumstances.

> *I tried to give up but I get too aggressive, I get uptight with the children, I used to cry. I could give up anti-depressants but not cigarettes. I took it out on my husband when I tried to give up. I just feel really let down without a cigarette.*
>
> Mother in social class IV/V [v]

Figure 3.4   Smoking prevalence among married and cohabiting women aged 16 to 34, by presence of dependent children, 1990, Britain

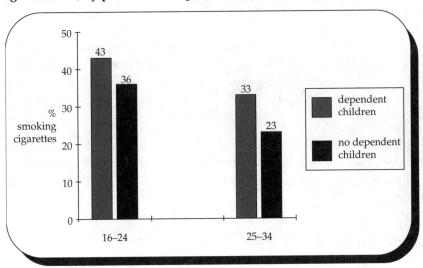

Source: derived from OPCS (1992) *General Household Survey 1990*, Table 6.14(b). HMSO.

The limited research on smoking and caring suggests that smoking is linked to features of caring which make it both different from and more stressful than other kinds of paid and unpaid work. For psychiatric nurses, for example, high levels of smoking have been linked to a high incidence of boredom and stress at work, with smoking providing a way of managing these aspects of their working lives. Cigarette smoking is also a means by which social relations are established and maintained between staff and patients [40]. Within the domestic setting, mothers with young children have described their smoking behaviour in similar ways. They have described how cigarettes mark out breaks from caring. Cigarettes and coffee breaks provide anticipated and structured times when mothers can rest and refuel [2, 32, 33].

> I smoke when I'm sitting down, having a cup of coffee. It's part and parcel of resting. Definitely, because it doesn't bother me if I haven't got cigarette when I'm working. If I can keep working, doing the housework and the washing and the ironing and things like that, and I'm busy, I won't bother smoking but if I'm sitting down chatting or sitting having a cup of coffee, then I smoke. If I'm busy, it doesn't bother me, but it's nice to sit down afterwards and have a cigarette.
>
> *Mother with pre-school children [vi]*

> Smoking is time for myself. In the morning I have a cigarette, but I wait till I'm back from taking Sue to school. Then I can sit down with a cup of tea and a little time sorting myself out for the day.
>
> *Lone mother [vii]*

> After Julie is in bed, we'll sit down as often as not and watch telly and I'll smoke a cigarette. I always have, even when I was working. It's my way of saying, 'that's it. I've done my work for today'.
>
> *Expectant mother [viii]*

As the accounts above suggest, cigarette smoking provides a way of making and marking time for oneself. It can symbolise adult time and entry into a social life which is not exclusively focused on childcare [32, 33].

> Joan usually comes around 10 ish and we have a coffee and a chat. That's when I smoke really, when she comes round. Her children play with mine and we have a good old natter.
>
> *Expectant mother [ix]*

Providing a way of structuring time and containing their domestic responsibilities, mothers have described how cigarette smoking is used to control their mood [41]. The accounts they have given researchers highlight how smoking helps them cope with a daily life that can be both stressful and monotonous.

> I smoke less when I'm not with others, a lot of it's out of boredom. I don't go out much, about once a fortnight, so I'm here on my own every night once the baby's in bed.

> I'm a heavier smoker because I'm in all day. I don't go out, don't drink and don't have a car. It's the only pleasure I have.

> I think it's because I'm bored, I smoke. I have no one else to talk to. I don't go out in the evenings. I feel a lot better when I'm busy. I don't have a lot of friends around here.
>
> Mothers in social class IV and V [x]

Recent studies have pointed to one particularly crucial aspect of the mood-management functions of smoking for women with young children. They have noted how smoking is experienced as a way of coping with stress and anger: a way of re-imposing order and calm when mothers feel their energy and patience is giving way [32, 33, 41].

When faced with demands they cannot meet, mothers have described how they create a space – symbolic if not real – between them and their children and fill this space with a self-directed activity. Smoking a cigarette provides a self-directed activity which can be instantly accessed when mothers feel that their breaking point has been reached [2, 33]. A recent national survey of mothers with children under the age of seven underlined how central cigarette smoking can be to the management of anger and the avoidance of physical abuse. Over 70% of the smokers felt that smoking helped them to calm down when they felt like smacking their children [42].

> I send them up to their bedroom when they're getting too much for me. When I see the danger signs looming, I think they're best out of the way. I sit down and have a cigarette and a cup of tea. After 10 minutes, I feel guilty and call them down. Usually the crisis has passed by them.

> Sometimes I put him outside the room, shut the door and put the radio on full blast and I've sat down and had a cigarette, calmed down and fetched him in again.
>
> Mothers with pre-school children [xi].

Qualitative studies, both in Britain and the US, have recorded how mothers caring in circumstances of hardship often identify smoking cigarettes as the only time they have to themselves and the only activity they do for themselves [2, 27, 33–5, 41].

> *I just gotta have cigarettes by my side 'cause they're the only stable thing in my life … Just not having them is the hardest thing. I won't smoke them, but I've gotta have them 'cause they're my best friend …*
>
> *Young expectant mother [xii]*

> *I couldn't face a day without cigarettes. That's all we've got now.*

> *My husband goes out three times a week drinking with his mates. I don't go. Smoking is my form of relaxation …*

> *My boyfriend has his pleasure. He drinks. The only pleasure I have is smoking.*

> *It's the only thing I do myself isn't it? I have to do things for the baby and for my husband, but smoking is about the only thing I can do for myself.*
>
> *Mothers under the age of 20 [xiii].*

Recognising that psycho-social factors like stress and isolation can make it hard to achieve long-term changes in health-related behaviour, research has given increasing attention to the role of social support in improving well-being. Professional support, intimate relationships, family networks and friendship ties are seen to mitigate the effects of an adverse social environment, protecting individual health and supporting health-promoting patterns of behaviour [26, 33, 42, 43]. The association between smoking status and social support is explored in the survey discussed in Part II.

3.6 Summary

The evidence on trends in cigarette smoking reviewed in Part I suggests that cigarette smoking is linked to dimensions of social disadvantage. As smoking prevalence has declined, the proportion of women in the smoking population has risen. At the same time, socio-economic differences in smoking prevalence have widened, with the result that working class women make up an increasingly significant sub-group of Britain's smoking population. Most of these female smokers are White. Despite the fact that women from minority ethnic groups are disproportionately found in manual households and in households with an unemployed head, smoking prevalence rates are low among Asian and African-Caribbean women.

Caring for others is also linked to smoking among women. Young women and lone mothers, groups in which disadvantage is clustered, have particularly high smoking prevalence rates and particularly low cessation rates. As the comments of maternal smokers make clear, cigarette smoking appears to be meshed into the ways in which women cope with living and caring in circumstances of disadvantage.

Notes
i.   Wells J (1987) *Women and Smoking: an Evaluation of the Role of Stress in Smoking Cessation and Relapse,* Southampton: Department of Psychology, University of Southampton, p11.

ii.   Graham H (1976) 'Smoking in pregnancy: the attitudes of pregnant mothers', *Social Science and Medicine,* 10: 403.

iii.   Oakley A (1989) 'Smoking in pregnancy: smokescreen or risk factor? Towards a materialist analysis', *Sociology of Health and Illness,* 11, 4: 321.

iv.   Wells, op cit p11 and 5.

v.   ibid.

vi.   Graham H (1993) *Hardship and Health in Women's Lives,* London: Harvester Wheatsheaf, p182.

vii.   Nicotinell (1993) *Smoking Mothers with Young Children: the Hidden Dilemma,* p32.

viii.   Graham H (1976), op cit, p403.

ix.   ibid, p403.

x.   Wells, op.cit, p11.

xi.   Graham H (1988) 'Women and smoking in the United Kingdom: the implications for health promotion', *Health Promotion,* 3, 4: 379.

xii.   Lawson E (1993) *The Role of Smoking in the Lives of Low-income Pregnant Adolescents,* Kentucky: Department of Behavioral Science, University of Kentucky, p12.

xiii.   Simms M and Smith C (1986) *Teenage Mothers and Their Partners,* London: HMSO, p78–9.

Part II
The Study of Working Class Mothers

Chapter 4

Introducing the study

4.1 Introduction

The patterns mapped out in Part I suggest that the decline in smoking prevalence in Britain has been associated with profound changes in its gender and class distribution. Gender differences have narrowed to the point where cigarette smoking has all but lost its male identity, with caring for others emerging as one of the threads that links women and smoking. Class differences have widened, giving cigarette smoking an increasingly strong working class identity. As a result of these trends, White working class women have become an important sub-group within the smoking population.

The study sheds light on how being a woman and being working class connects with smoking behaviour. Based on a sample of 905 women with young children in working class households, it was designed to identify the social, material and personal factors linked to smoking status.

The sections below introduce the study, looking in turn at its aims and methods and at the mothers who took part.

4.2 Purpose of the study

The survey was designed to contribute to the development of health promotion and smoking cessation policies which are sensitive to the factors associated with smoking and non-smoking among working class women with children. The study explored the connections between cigarette smoking and dimensions of mothers' everyday lives. It focused on whether and in what ways smoking was linked to the responsibilities that structured women's daily lives and to the circumstances in which they worked to meet them. It examined four specific dimensions of mothers' lives:–

> *everyday responsibilities:* child care responsibilities, caring responsibilities for other family members, patterns of paid work;

material circumstances: housing circumstances, partner's employment, income and benefit status, debt and budgeting, access to a car/van and telephone;

social support and networks: relationships with partner, family and friendship networks, religious beliefs, feelings of belonging to the neighbourhood;

personal and health resources: physical and psycho-social health, health knowledge and beliefs, patterns of health-related behaviour and alternative coping strategies.

4.3   Design of the study

905 mothers took part in the study, which was conducted across 1990 and 1991. The mothers lived in the catchment areas of two large maternity hospitals in Nottingham and Coventry and were interviewed at home when their babies were 6 months old. The study was designed to include White and African-Caribbean women. However, only White mothers were recruited to the Coventry arm of the study. As a result, the majority of the sample (97%) identified themselves as White.

The sample was drawn from women whose ante-natal records suggested that they met the occupational criteria for inclusion in the study. Because only a small proportion of married and cohabiting mothers had details of their occupation included in their hospital records, it was not possible to construct these criteria around women's occupation. Instead, eligibility was determined in the conventional way, on the basis of the occupation of head of household, with the male partners of married and cohabiting women treated as the head of household. This method means that women of different marital statuses were classified in different ways, with the employment position and occupation of single women central to their class position while the employment position and occupation of married women played no part in determining their class position [1–3]. Despite the limitations of the classification, surveys have found that it produces clear trends for factors linked both to living standards, like tenure and household income, and to health and health-related behaviour [4–5].

The mothers eligible to enter the study were:

- mothers living with a partner whose occupation fell into social class 3M (skilled manual), 4 (semi-skilled manual) or 5 (unskilled manual) or who was unemployed.

- lone mothers whose occupation fell into social class 3M, 4 or 5 or whose occupational status was listed as housewife or unemployed.

The sample was stratified by smoking status, with smokers defined as those who smoked at least one cigarette a day. An analysis of patient records suggested that 44% of women in the two centres who met the selection criteria were smokers. The stratification process meant that just over half (52%) of the mothers interviewed reported that they were smokers.

Of the 1,382 mothers approached, 905 (66%) agreed to take part in the study. Of the non-responders, 270 (57%) refused, 143 (30%) did not have a traceable address and 64 (13%) were not at home after three call-back visits. Analysis of the non-responders suggests that there were no significant differences between the mothers who took part in the study and either those who refused or those who were not in after three visits. Women who had no traceable address were younger, more likely to be single and to have no-one in their household listed as employed than the mothers who participated in the survey.

Mothers were interviewed at home. The interview included fixed-choice questions, where mothers selected the response that most closely fitted their situation from a list read out by the interviewer, and open-ended questions, where mothers were invited to highlight the issues and experiences they considered to be the most important for them. Information on psychological well-being collected during the interviews was supplemented by data from the 12-item General Health Questionnaire (GHQ). 899 mothers, 99% of the total, completed the GHQ-12. The 12-item GHQ, like the standard 30-item version, is concerned with a person's current mental state, dealing with such dimensions as anxiety, depression, sleep disturbance and general life satisfaction. The questionnaire has been used to estimate the prevalence of psychiatric disorder in the population, with validity studies designed to establish the appropriate threshold [6]. Validation studies of the GHQ-12 point to a score between 2 and 3 as indicating possible cases of psychiatric disorder [7, 8]. As in the longer version of the GHQ, this threshold results in a high prevalence of possible cases of psychiatric illness among women [4]. This has led researchers to conclude that the threshold value may be set too low, with further validation studies required to estimate a higher threshold for possible psychiatric illness [9].

A number of points should be noted about the survey design and the analysis of results. The results are subject to the sampling errors associated with random stratified samples. Non-response bias will also affect the results, with non-response among mothers with no traceable address skewed towards those with high smoking prevalence. The survey relied on self-reported data and therefore reflected subjective assessments of caring responsibilities, material circumstances and smoking status. A review of self-reported smoking behaviour concluded that self-reports were reliable and valid, except where there were strong social influences that made it desirable to understate prevalence and under-estimate consumption [10]. Questions about smoking behaviour were introduced as part of a broader survey of the experiences of mothers with young children, and represented only a relatively small part of the survey. Interviewed when their babies were 6 months old, the feelings of guilt some women experience about smoking in pregnancy should also have been reduced. Both these factors are likely to have encouraged accurate reporting of smoking behaviour.

Because of the higher sampling fraction of smokers, characteristics which are associated with smoking are likely to be over-represented in the sample. The section below should be read with this in mind. The subsequent chapters in Part II avoid generalisations based on the sample as a whole, focusing on the patterns of association between smoking behaviour and the mothers' material and social circumstances.

One final caveat should be noted. The evidence from the survey points to strong associations between the circumstances of mothers' daily lives and their smoking status. These associations, however, do not demonstrate a direct causal pathway. The processes linking current circumstances and current smoking status are likely to be much more complex. For example, current smoking behaviour reflects past smoking behaviour: most of the mothers in the study took up smoking in adolescence. Further, cigarette smoking exerts an independent influence on many of the factors with which it is associated. For example, the association between smoking and having financial difficulties is likely to reflect, at least in part, the heavy financial burden which cigarette smoking imposes on low-income households. Similarly, cigarette smoking may be both cause and effect of the poorer physical and emotional well-being of the mothers who reported themselves as smokers. The interaction between smoking and other dimensions of women's lives means that, while associations can be identified, any conclusions about the direction of causality must be cautiously drawn.

4.4 The mothers in the study

The sample was composed primarily of young women for whom the care of their families was their primary responsibility. The majority of the mothers (80%) were under 30. Most (61%) were caring for other children in addition to their six month old baby. A very small minority (4%) were in full-time employment. The remainder reported that they cared for their baby on a more or less full-time basis. The majority of the mothers were living with a partner. Among this group of cohabiting mothers was one mother who identified herself as living with a female partner. A sizeable minority (23%) were lone mothers.

The patterns of housing tenure, employment and income point to a sample facing the kind of experiences that go with parenthood in White working class communities in 1990s Britain. Just under half (49%) of the mothers lived in owner-occupied housing. A third (33%) of the sample were in receipt of income support; a further 11% were receiving family credit. The high proportion of mothers on income support reflected both the number of lone mothers in the sample and the relatively high levels of male unemployment. Among those living with partners, one in five (20%) had partners who were not in paid work. In the sample as a whole, a third (34%) of the households had no-one in employment. A large minority of mothers reported that they were facing economic hardship: four in ten (43%) reported debts and three in ten (34%) were cutting back on what they spent in order to try and make ends meet.

While access to material resources was a significant problem for many mothers, most mothers reported high levels of social contact and support. The majority of the mothers were living, or in a steady relationship, with a partner (90%) and were in weekly contact with their mothers (88%). The majority (71%) of the respondents reported that there were friends and/or neighbours to whom they felt very close and the same proportion reported seeing their friends at least once a week. Taking their social networks as a whole, only 2% of the sample stated that they had no-one at all to whom they felt close. However, a much higher proportion, 40% of the sample, reported that isolation was a problem that they had experienced over the previous year. A significant proportion, 25% of the total, had experienced the death of a close relative or friend in the past year.

Turning to the mothers' personal resources, most mothers (72%) assessed their health as excellent or good. However, over a quarter assessed their health as only fair or poor. The symptoms checklist uncovered a greater incidence of health problems, with 44% of the mothers reporting backache and headaches and over half reporting that they felt tired all the time. One in three (35%) of the mothers scored three or more on the GHQ-12, suggesting a high prevalence of psycho-social problems and possible psychiatric illness. While a high prevalence, it is in line with the findings of other studies. The national Health and Lifestyle Survey used the longer 30-item GHQ and found that 32% of married women with dependent children who were not in paid work were above the threshold [11].

There was a widespread awareness of the health-risks of smoking. Nine in ten mothers (90%) stated unequivocally that smoking was bad for people's health. A similarly high proportion (85%) stated unequivocally that parental smoking is bad for the health of the children in the household. The respondents also demonstrated a high level of awareness of the specific health-risks faced by smokers. Nine in ten (92%) of the mothers thought that smokers were more likely to get lung cancer than non-smokers.

These patterns of belief and knowledge about smoking match those uncovered in national surveys. In contrast to the 1960s, the vast majority of the population today accept the general health risks of smoking and are knowledgeable about its specific health risks [12-15]. The patterns found among the population as a whole are reflected in the health-beliefs and health-knowledge of women in lower socio-economic groups. Thus, a national British survey conducted in the early 1980s found that 92% of women aged 16 to 40 who lived in manual households believed that there was a connection between smoking and health [13]. Similarly, in a more recent national survey, 90% of women aged 18 to 39 stated that lung cancer is caused by smoking. The proportion was higher among women with educational qualifications than among those without [14].

The chapters that follow explore the factors which may explain why mothers in manual households continue to smoke, despite an awareness of its health risks. They examine the associations between smoking status and dimensions of the mothers' everyday lives, weaving their own accounts into the analysis. The mothers are identified by their household status, as single mothers (mothers living alone as unmarried, separated, divorced and widowed mothers) and mothers living with a partner (married and cohabiting mothers).

Chapter 5

Patterns of smoking
and ex-smoking

5.1   Introduction

The chapter maps out the patterns of smoking among the mothers in
the survey. The section below provides an overview of their smoking
habits. Sections 5.3 and 5.4 look in more detail at the mothers who
reported themselves to be current smokers, describing their smoking
careers and the place of smoking in their everyday lives. The second
part of the chapter is concerned with mothers' experiences of smoking cessation, and considers in turn the unsuccessful attempts of the
current smokers (section 5.5) and the lives and lifestyles of the small
group of mothers who had successfully given up smoking (section
5.6).

5.2   Smoking prevalence and consumption

The survey was designed to ensure that at least half of the mothers
were cigarette smokers. The sampling procedure, outlined in chapter
4, resulted in a higher proportion of smokers in the study than in the
population from which it was drawn. A cigarette smoker was defined
as someone who usually smoked one or more cigarettes a day. On
this criterion, 52% of mothers were smokers. A further 14% were ex-
smokers. Thus, two-thirds (66%) of the sample were current smokers
or had been smokers in the past (Figure 5.1). As noted in chapter 4,
the majority of mothers in the study defined themselves as White.
Ethnic identity was not, however, strongly linked to smoking status.
Among White mothers, 52% reported that they were smokers; among
the 19 mothers who identified themselves as Black, 10 (53%) stated
that they smoked one or more cigarettes a day.

The patterns of reported cigarette consumption are described in
Figure 5.2. The figure suggests that two-thirds (66%) of the current
smokers smoked less than 20 cigarettes a day, with nearly half smoking between 10 and 19 cigarettes a day. Just over a third of the smok-

ers reported smoking 20 cigarettes or more a day. The mean number of cigarettes smoked a day by mothers in this high consumption group was 22, suggesting that there were few very heavy smokers. The proportion of smokers smoking 20 or more cigarettes a day is in line with patterns recorded in the General Household Survey (GHS). In the GHS, a third (34%) of the female smokers in manual socio-economic groups were heavy smokers in 1990, smoking 20 or more cigarettes a day [1].

Figure 5.1   Mothers' current smoking status   (n = 905)

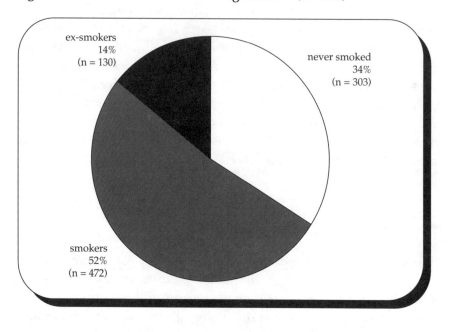

5.3   Current smokers: smoking careers and beliefs

Like most smokers in Britain, the majority of the smokers in the study reported that they were smoking regularly by the time they were eighteen. Four in five (81%) were regular smokers by this age, with most smokers taking up regular smoking between the age of 14 and 17 (Figure 5.3). The mean age of becoming a regular smoker was 15.7 years.

National surveys indicate that the vast majority of female smokers in Britain smoke filter cigarettes. Estimates based on the GHS suggest that, in the 16 to 34 age group, 98% of female smokers mainly smoke filter cigarettes [1]. The proportion was matched in the survey, with

Figure 5.2   Number of cigarettes smoked a day   (n = 472)

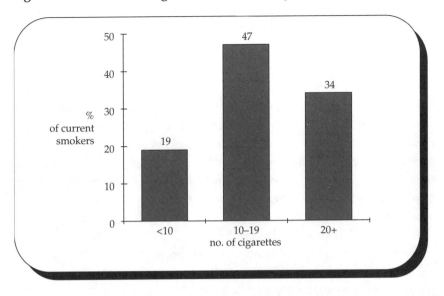

98% of the smokers stating that they bought filter-tipped cigarettes, typically in the middle and middle to low tar range. Most smokers (93%) reported that they inhaled. The proportion of mothers who

Figure 5.3   Age at which current smokers started to smoke regularly (n = 472)

Photo-copy

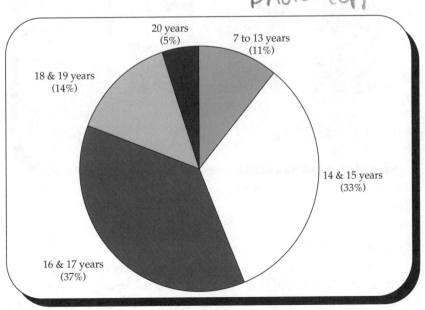

reported inhaling was lower among those smoking less than 10 cigarettes a day (85%) than among mothers smoking more heavily (95%)
(p <0.005).

Confirming patterns uncovered in other studies, cigarette smokers
were likely to report that key members of their family and friendship
networks were smokers [2–4]. The majority of current smokers with
partners reported that their partners smoked (73%), a proportion significantly higher than among the non-smokers (41%). A significantly
higher proportion of current smokers than non-smokers also reported
that most or all of their close friends smoked. More smokers than
non-smokers reported that one or both of their parents were smokers
when the respondent was growing up. It should be noted, however,
that a family background of smoking was not limited to the current
smokers. As Figure 5.4 indicates, a high proportion of both smokers
(86%) and non-smokers (80%) reported that one or both parents were
regular smokers during their childhood.

**Figure 5.4   Patterns of smoking among family and friendship
networks   (n = 905)**

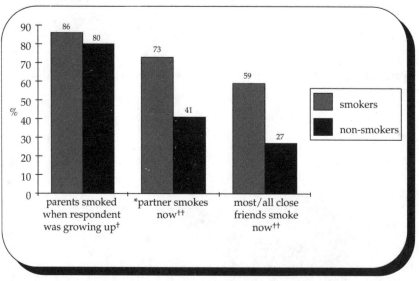

* respondents living with partner only, n = 689

† < 0.01

†† < 0.001

Nine in ten of the mothers bought their own cigarettes, with smokers
consuming less than 10 cigarettes a day significantly less likely to buy
their own than other smokers (p <0.01). For the small minority who
did not purchase their cigarettes themselves, it was their partner who

typically bought them. For the majority of mothers, buying cigarettes was something that they did as part of their general shopping. Only one in four (26%) of the smokers reported that they typically made special trips to buy their cigarettes.

Health beliefs

It was noted in chapter 4 that there was a widespread recognition of the general health risks of smoking and of the links between smoking and specific diseases. These patterns of health beliefs and knowledge were reproduced among the smokers and non-smokers. However, the smokers were consistently less likely to hold an anti-smoking line. Thus, while the majority of smokers and non-smokers agreed that smoking was bad for health, there was a larger minority of smokers (19%) than non-smokers (10%) who did not agree with this view. Similarly, the majority who agreed that parental smoking was bad for the health of children in the household was smaller among the smokers (69%) than the non-smokers (85%). These health beliefs are mapped out in Figure 5.5. The figure records that a large majority of smokers and non-smokers also felt that smokers were more likely to get lung cancer and heart disease than people who did not smoke. As it indicates, non-smokers were again more likely to hold these health beliefs about the adverse effects of smoking than smokers.

Figure 5.5   Health beliefs about smoking   (n = 905)

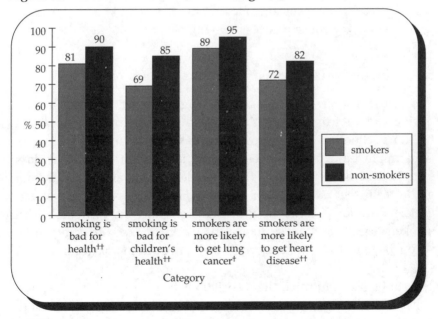

† < 0.05

†† < 0.001

Other surveys have found less pronounced differences in the beliefs of smokers and non-smokers. A national survey conducted in the early 1980s suggested that smoking status was not strongly linked to the health beliefs of women aged 16 to 40 in manual households. In this group, 90% of the smokers and 92% of the non-smokers believed that smoking was a threat to health. Among adults as a whole, more smokers than non-smokers believed that there was a general connection between smoking and illness [5]. This finding has been confirmed in more recent surveys. In the Health and Lifestyle Survey, smokers appeared to be more conscious of the general health-risks of smoking and of its links to specific diseases, like heart disease and bronchitis [6].

However, like these national surveys, the study of working class mothers underlines the fact that the vast majority of smokers continue to smoke in the face of knowledge and beliefs about its health risks. Underlining this mismatch between beliefs and behaviour, less than half (45%) of the smokers reported that they cut down their consumption when they became pregnant. Comparing their consumption 6 months after birth with their consumption during pregnancy, two-thirds (63%) of the smokers reported that their consumption when pregnant was the same or higher than it was now. Stress and boredom figured centrally in their accounts of why their consumption was not lower when they were pregnant. Such findings lend weight to earlier studies which have suggested that there are mechanisms at work which sustain smoking in the face of knowledge of its health-damaging consequences [4, 7–12].

5.4   The everyday lives of current smokers

The evidence reviewed in chapter 3 suggests that smoking before, during and after pregnancy is associated with having fewer years of full-time schooling and fewer qualifications [2–4, 10]. These associations might be expected to be less pronounced in a working class sample, where the majority of mothers left school at 16 and did not go on to further education or training. However, as Figure 5.6 suggests, educational differences are still strongly in evidence, with smokers significantly less likely than non-smokers to stay on at school beyond 16 and to undertake further education or training.

The study also confirmed the associations between smoking, age and marital status uncovered in other surveys of mothers [4, 10–14]. Smoking was linked to being younger and to being a lone mother. As Figure 5.7 records, the mothers who were current smokers were more likely to be under the age of 25 and to be lone mothers. They were more likely to be bringing up their children in households with limited access to income and material resources, with a higher proportion of smokers than non-smokers living in households on income support and without a telephone.

Figure 5.6   Educational background of current smokers and non-smokers   (n = 905)

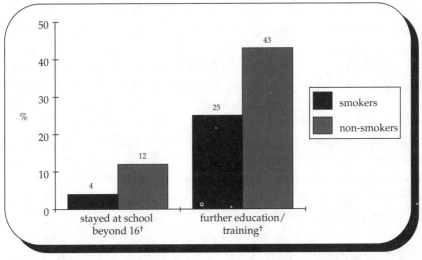

† p < 0.001

Figure 5.7   Social background and circumstances of current smokers and non-smokers   (n = 905)

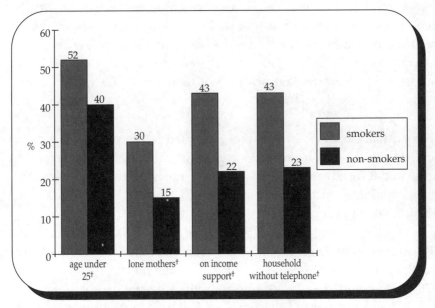

† p < 0.001

Interestingly, these differences in the social background and material circumstances of smokers and non-smokers did not appear to extend to the respondents' family and social networks. For example, a similar proportion of smokers and non-smokers had both their parents alive, were in contact with their mothers and rated their relationships with them as very close. Among respondents living with a partner, a similar proportion also felt that they could confide in him/her about personal problems. A similar proportion of the smokers and non-smokers also reported that they had close friends and saw their friends at least once a week.

The similarities in the social networks and social lives of the smokers and non-smokers give way to differences when the findings on health status and well-being are considered. Smokers were less likely to report excellent health than non-smokers; the proportions were 14% and 24% respectively (p <0.001). This may reflect objective differences in health status, differences which may be affected, at least in part, by differences in smoking behaviour. However, it may also reflect an inclination among the smokers to rate their health as fair or poor simply because they smoke.

Measures of psycho-social health also suggest poorer health status among the current smokers. More smokers than non-smokers reported periods of feeling isolated (45% compared with 34%). Conversely, a smaller proportion of smokers (72%) than non-smokers (80%) felt that they had choice and control over the way in which their lives were turning out (p <0.001). These differences in mothers' feelings of well-being are captured in the patterns of response to the General Health Questionnaire. A significantly higher proportion of smokers than non-smokers scored 3 or more on the GHQ: 41% compared with 29% (p <0.001).

The evidence reviewed in chapter 3 pointed to the place of cigarette smoking in the lives of mothers caring for children in circumstances of material disadvantage and poor psycho-social health. It suggests that smoking is part of the way in which women structure time for themselves and keep going under stress [8–11].

The survey confirmed the links between cigarette smoking and the routines of mothers' lives. The majority of the mothers who smoked (78%) reported that there were certain times of the day or situations when they were more likely to smoke. Follow-up questions sought to identify the times and situations in which the smokers felt they were very or fairly likely to want to smoke. Their answers, which provided the set of responses in Figure 5.8, suggested times and situations closely associated with caring for young children. Significant among these were visiting a friend or neighbour (63%), having time to one-self (90%) and feeling on edge (90%). Among the everyday situations the mothers identified with smoking, the last two stand out. The majority of the smokers reported that they were 'very likely' to smoke when they had time to themselves and when they were feeling on edge (Figure 5.8).

Figure 5.8 Times when current smokers report that they are likely to smoke

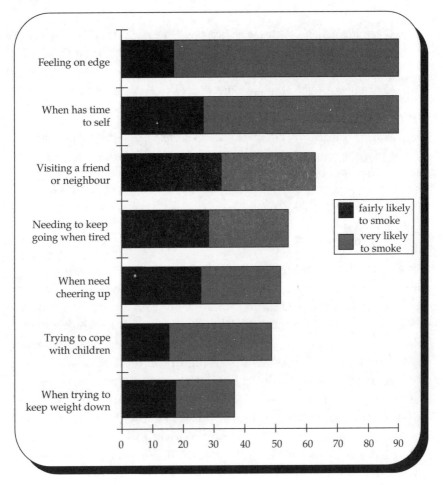

The accounts that mothers gave illustrate how closely smoking was linked to caring-breaks and to mood control, with mothers describing their smoking as something they did when they had time to themselves and when they felt under stress. The social dimensions of smoking also figured strongly in their answers.

> *Times or situations mothers identified as ones in which they were very likely to want to smoke.*

> *In the evening, sometimes I can sit down then. I'm always on the go but I grab one when I sit down.*

> *In the afternoon when she has gone to bed and I can sit down for a few minutes.*

> *I have noticed when something gets on top of me, I light a fag up and relax.*

> *When I'm making the tea. The two older ones come home from school, the baby's hungry and all four of them are hungry. They are all fighting and screaming in here and the dinner's cooking in the kitchen. I'm ready to blow up so I light up a cigarette. It calms me down when I'm under so much stress.*

> *When I'm drinking, I'm more inclined to smoke. When I have a cup of tea and when my mum comes over. When my husband smokes and he smokes heavily. So around 5.00pm when my husband comes in.*

5.5 Trying to give up smoking

As Figure 5.8 indicates, the majority of the current smokers recognised that there were a range of everyday situations in which they were likely to smoke. Despite the centrality that mothers accorded to cigarette smoking, the majority had tried to give it up. Three-quarters (76%) had tried at least once. Mothers were asked an open-ended question about their reasons for giving up on the last occasion, with categories of answers built up out of the accounts they gave. Health-related reasons figured strongly in mothers' accounts of why they tried to give up smoking (Figure 5.9). When asked about the factors that had prompted their last attempt to give up smoking, four in ten (43%) gave reasons linked to the health of their baby and their children and a quarter (26%) gave reasons linked to their own health. The only other major category of response concerned the cost of smoking. A quarter (27%) of the mothers gave financial reasons as the main factor for their most recent attempt to give up smoking.

Figure 5.9 Main reasons why current smokers tried to give up smoking on the last occasion (n = 355)

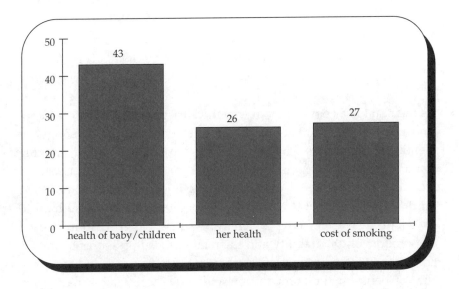

Note: more than one response possible

What were your reasons for wanting to give up smoking on this last occasion?

I thought it would be better for the baby, bearing in mind that everything we take in goes into their blood stream. And my boyfriend thought I smoked too much, which I did.

Mother living with partner

Just because of being pregnant; I thought it might hurt the baby. I packed up for a couple of weeks and then got down to five a day. Everyone was nagging me about low birthweight and everything. My older one was 8½lbs and this baby was 8lbs, so it's not always true.

Mother living with partner

I couldn't face smoking. I was a bit run down and I couldn't stand the smell. I just had enough of it. I just grab a cigarette when I'm upset about something and I generally feel awful when I've been with people who smoke. And money reasons. If we both gave up smoking, we'd save at least £20 a week.

Mother living with partner

Because of what happened to my mum. When she died I wanted to live a more healthy life and take care of myself.

Single mother

I was with my husband then and we were buying about 60 a day and it was the money angle. No other reason, just the expense.

Single mother

As their status as current smokers indicates, their attempts to give up smoking had been unsuccessful. An open-ended question sought to identify why mothers who had tried to give up, had started smoking again. The major reasons mothers gave for starting again clustered around the difficulty of managing their lives without cigarettes. A third of the mothers (31%) said it was because they found it hard to cope with their everyday problems and stress. Other reasons focused on boredom and irritability and the related social pressures to smoke, either direct interpersonal pressure from partners or the indirect pressure of being in the company of smokers. These factors have been identified in previous studies as important in smoking relapse [4, 8, 15]. In amplifying their answers, mothers' accounts give a further insight into the clustering of influences and pressures that can make it hard to remain a non-smoker.

Table 5.1: **Smoking relapse: mothers' answers to the question 'why did you start smoking again?'**   **(n = 355)**

	% of mothers giving response	(no. of responses)
coping with problems and stress	31	(109)
social reasons and pressure	23	(83)
hard habit to break	21	(73)
restarted activity linked to smoking	9	(33)
boredom	8	(29)
never really gave up	6	(22)
enjoy smoking	5	(19)
to keep weight down	5	(19)
don't know	5	(16)
other	1	(2)

Note: more than one response possible

Why did you start smoking again?

My husband encouraged me to start again. Once I had the baby I was on edge, I needed something to calm me down.

> *Mother living with partner*

It's difficult not to lose your temper and with four of them now it's worse. I was shouting at them and taking it out on them for no reason. When I saw my friends smoking at the school gate, it was hard not to.

> *Mother living with partner*

I couldn't give up so I just cut down. I was getting irritable and losing my temper a lot and I found a cigarette calmed me down.

> *Single mother*

Stress, it helped calm me down. Gradually I crept up to this level. Mind you, I was smoking about 30 a day before I was pregnant. I was putting on too much weight. When I gave up I was nibbling. Then I went out one night and had one and that was it. My partner smokes as well and I find it hard sitting beside him. It would be easier to stop if no one else smoked. I just couldn't help myself.

> *Mother living with partner*

I started to eat more of the wrong food – chocolates and crisps. When I smoke, it calms me down when I have a problem. I couldn't cope with the dizziness. If I stood up I would feel dizzy – regularly. Or if I walked too fast. Also domestic problems. My boyfriend wasn't too thrilled that I was pregnant and there were constant arguments about whether I should have the baby or not.

> *Mother living with partner*

As the accounts of the mothers who tried to give up smoking suggest, smoking is a habit that is hard to break. This resistance to change was underlined in other ways. It was underlined by the fact that a quarter (25%) of the mothers reported that they had never tried to give up smoking. It comes across, too, in the patterns of cessation-attempts. Only four in ten (41%) of the current smokers in the study had attempted to give up smoking during pregnancy and early motherhood, a period which health professionals have identified as offering unrivalled opportunities for initiating behavioural change. While seen as rich in health promotion opportunities by professionals, it was a period in which 60% of the current smokers reported that they did not attempt to give up smoking (Table 5.2).

Table 5.2: Current smokers' attempts at giving up smoking   (n = 472)

	%
Not tried at least once to give up	25
Tried, but not since she became pregnant	35
Tried since she became pregnant	41
Total	**100**

As other studies have suggested, tobacco consumption has a significant effect on women's cessation behaviour. While those smoking more than 20 cigarettes a day were as likely to have tried to give up altogether, those smoking less than 20 cigarettes a day were more likely to have succeeded in giving up for more than a week. Low smokers were also more likely to have tried to give up since they became pregnant than the high smokers. Nearly half of those smoking less than 20 cigarettes a day (47%) had tried to stop smoking in the fifteen months prior to the interview. Among the high smokers, the proportion was 29%.

Perhaps reflecting the fact that most of the current smokers had tried unsuccessfully to give up smoking, the majority strongly agreed that smoking was a habit that was hard to break. Only one in seven smokers (14%) disagreed with the statement that smoking is a habit that is hard to break.

Why did you start smoking again?

I went back to work. It's just a habit while I was at work.

I needed one. I couldn't cope without one. I felt all irritable without having one.

Since the baby was born, you feel at the end of your tether and a cigarette made me feel better, helps me cope. I feel it's better than throwing him about and tearing my hair out.

I wanted to. I enjoy a cigarette. My friends all smoke and I get a bit irritable if I give up for any length of time. It acts as a safety valve for me really.

5.6   Patterns of ex-smoking

As noted at the beginning of the chapter, two-thirds (66%) of mothers had a history of cigarette smoking (Figure 5.1). Of this group of 602 mothers, a relatively small proportion (21%) were ex-smokers. One in four (25%) of the ex-smokers had given up smoking during their last pregnancy. However, for most of this group (68%), giving up smoking was an event which occurred before their last pregnancy (Figure 5.10).

The patterns summarised in Figure 5.10 confirm the patterns identified among the current smokers and suggest that pregnancy and early motherhood was a period which saw little change in smoking status. Of the 514 women who reported themselves to be smokers during their last pregnancy, 92% were still smokers by the time their baby reached 6 months old.

Figure 5.10   When ex-smokers gave up smoking   (n = 130)

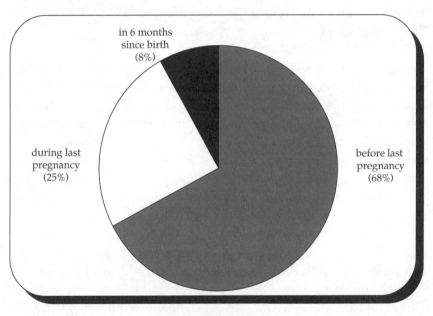

There were important differences in the smoking careers and smoking habits of the ex-smokers and current smokers. As other studies have confirmed, successful cessation was associated with a later onset of regular smoking [16]. By their 16th birthday, when 45% of the current smokers were regular smokers, only a third (35%) of the ex-smokers were smoking regularly. The mean age for regular cigarette smoking for ex-smokers was 17.5 years, nearly two years older than the mean for current smokers (15.7 years).

There were no differences in the proportion of ex-smokers and current smokers who reported that their parents had smoked during their childhood. There were, however, significant differences in the smoking behaviour of partners. As other studies have reported, successful cessation was strongly associated with having a non-smoking partner (p <0.001) [12, 16, 17]. Again, in line with other studies, the ex-smokers in the survey differed with respect to their adult smoking habits [16, 18]. They reported a lower cigarette consumption than the current smokers. Among the current smokers, less than a fifth (19%) smoked less than 10 cigarettes a day: among the ex-smokers, over half (55%) smoked less than 10 a day. However, a similar proportion of current (34%) and ex-smokers (32%) were heavy smokers, reporting that they smoked 20 or more cigarettes a day. One ex-smoker reported smoking 60 a day. This suggests that, while most ex-smokers were recruited from the ranks of the light smokers, heavy smoking did not prevent women in the study from successfully giving up. The majority of the ex-smokers (57%) noted that they gave up smoking on their first attempt.

Taking up smoking later and smoking less, they were also slightly less likely to inhale than current smokers (89% compared with 92%). There was, however, no evidence to suggest that ex-smokers smoked lower-tar cigarettes than current smokers or that a larger proportion were smoking filter-tipped cigarettes. Like current smokers, most ex-smokers bought their own cigarettes. However, compared to current smokers, they were significantly less likely to buy their cigarettes as part of their general shopping and significantly more likely to make special trips to buy their cigarettes (p <0.01).

Other data also suggest that cigarette smoking was less deeply embedded in the lives of ex-smokers. Compared to the continuing smokers, the ex-smokers were significantly more likely to have previously quit for more than one week [19]. Previous quitting success has been found to be associated with successful long-term cessation in other studies [20]. They were also less likely to feel that there were particular times or situations where they were very likely to want a cigarette (69% compared with 78% for current smokers). As Figure 5.11 indicates, ex-smokers were consistently less likely to identify everyday situations as ones in which they were fairly or very likely to smoke. For example, in the everyday experiences of trying to cope with children or visiting a friend, around a quarter of the ex-smokers reported that they would have been fairly or very likely to smoke: among the current smokers, the proportions were 49% and 62%

respectively. Similarly, the ex-smokers were significantly less likely to report that they would be likely to smoke when they had time to themselves (53% compared with 90% of current smokers). The only situation in which ex-smokers scored highly was in response to the question about feeling on edge. Here, 83% reported that they would be fairly or very likely to smoke.

What sorts of times or situations were you very likely to want to smoke?

When I was tense or agitated. When my mum died. When the kids played up. Stress and circumstances, really.

When I was socialising – drinking. It seemed awful at first to be with other people and not to smoke, that was the main difficulty I found with packing it up.

Figure 5.11 Times when current and ex-smokers report that they are/were fairly or very likely to smoke

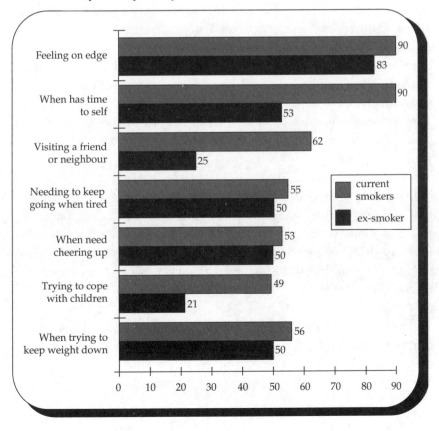

5.7 Summary

The patterns of smoking and ex-smoking uncovered in the study are in line with those mapped out in previous research on women's smoking. They suggest that cigarette smoking is deeply embedded in the past and present lives of many mothers in working class households. The established and routine nature of cigarette smoking was reflected in a variety of ways.

It was reflected, firstly, in the patterns of smoking among family and friends. Most smokers and non-smokers grew up in families in which one or both of their parents were smokers. Current smokers were significantly more likely to be living with partners who smoked. However, four in ten of the non-smokers also had partners who smoked.

Secondly, smoking was tied into the routines of everyday life. For most of the smokers, smoking was a well-established habit. A large majority were regular smokers by the time they were 18, and bought their cigarettes as part of their general shopping. Cigarette smoking was strongly associated with a variety of contexts linked to caring for young children, including the experience of feeling under stress and on edge. Smoking was a less well-established and routine feature of the lives of mothers who had given up smoking. They had started smoking later, and had smoked less and were less likely to buy their cigarettes as part of their general shopping than current smokers. They were also less likely to identify situations linked to the care of young children as ones in which they would have been very likely to want a cigarette.

Thirdly, the embedded nature of smoking was suggested by the fact that smokers continued to smoke in the face of knowledge of its health-damaging consequences. Despite this knowledge, the vast majority (92%) of respondents who reported themselves to be cigarette smokers at the start of their pregnancy, were still smokers at the time of the interview.

The next chapter looks more closely at the everyday lives of the mothers in the study, teasing out some of the links between smoking status and the circumstances and responsibilities which structure their experiences of caring for young children.

Chapter 6

Everyday responsibilities and material circumstances

6.1 Introduction

The survey focused on a group in the population in which smoking prevalence is known to be high. It is a group marked out by heavy caring responsibilities and low socio-economic status. The study sought to uncover and examine the associations between cigarette smoking and dimensions of mothers' everyday lives, looking at whether and how smoking status was linked to caring responsibilities and access to material, social and personal health resources (see section 4.2).

In order to explore these associations, the respondents were placed in one of four groups on the basis of their current smoking status (Table 6.1) The four groups were:

- mothers who had never smoked,

- ex-smokers,

- mothers currently smoking less than 20 cigarettes a day (light smokers),

- mothers smoking 20 or more cigarettes a day (heavy smokers).

It should be noted that, because of the way in which the sample was selected, over half of the mothers were light or heavy smokers.

Table 6.1: **The four smoking status groups (n = 905)**

	%	(No.)
Never smoked	34	(303)
Ex-smokers	14	(130)
Light smokers (<20 a day)	35	(312)
Heavy smokers (20+ a day)	18	(160)
	100	(905)

Chapters 6 and 7 examine the associations between smoking status and mothers' everyday lives. Beginning with a brief discussion of the social background of mothers in the four smoking status groups, this chapter focuses on mothers' everyday responsibilities and material circumstances; chapter 7 is concerned with their social networks and health resources. The accounts included in the sections below are all drawn from answers to a question about whether there were major problems which the mother had faced in the past twelve months.

6.2 Social background

As the patterns uncovered in Chapter 5 suggest, there were significant differences in the social backgrounds of the four groups. School leaving age was significantly related to smoking status, with a higher proportion of women staying on at school beyond 16 among the never smokers (12%) and ex-smokers (14%) than among the light smokers (4%) and heavy smokers (5%) (p <0.0001). Women who had never smoked were more likely (but not significantly more likely) to have parents who were non-smokers when they were growing up than women in the ex-smoking, light smoking and heavy smoking groups.

Among those living with a partner, there was a clear link between the mother's smoking status and the smoking status of her partner. This association is mapped out in Table 6.2. The age at which respondents took up regular smoking was also significantly related to their current smoking status. Light smokers were significantly younger than the other three groups, with an average age of 24, compared with 26 for the never, ex- and heavy smokers (p <0.001).

Table 6.2: **Partner's smoking status: the proportion of partners who are current smokers within the four smoking status groups (women living with partners only)   (n = 698)   (p <0.0001)**

	Partner is a current smoker %
Never smoked	40
Ex-smokers	44
Light smokers	74
Heavy smokers	71

6.3 Everyday responsibilities

As noted in chapter 4, childcare responsibilities were a dominant feature of the lives of the mothers in the sample. Most mothers were with their youngest child most of the day; few were in paid work. These patterns of responsibility did not vary significantly between the four smoking status groups.

A similar (and high) proportion of mothers in each group reported having their youngest child with them all day and not having had an evening out without their children in the last week. The patterns of employment did not differ significantly among the mothers in the four groups.

These similarities extended to mothers' assessments of the problems of caring for their children. There were no significant differences in the proportion stating that they found their youngest child hard to cope with or that they found themselves losing their temper with their children more easily than previously. However, smokers, and heavy smokers in particular, were more likely to report that they found the behaviour of one or more of their children hard to cope with.

Looking more broadly at mothers' caring responsibilities, more marked differences begin to emerge between the four smoking status groups. The number of children under 16 in the household was significantly related to heavy smoking (p <0.001). The mean number of children in the households of never, past and light smokers was 1.9; among heavy smokers, it was 2.3.

The reasons mothers who smoked more in pregnancy gave for their higher consumption

I more or less chain-smoked (in pregnancy). It was the other kids who caused the stress. I had three under 4 years and I was pregnant. It was just the pressures from the children. The worry about everything got me down. The kids, the house, the shopping. The worry about how I was going to cope with the new baby, having him so close to the others.
Mother living with partner, smoker

I don't know. Coping with the babies. I wasn't able to cope with two of them on my own, with my husband away (in prison).
Single mother, smoker

I think smoking is an escape route at times. For when you've a few min-utes when they're asleep.

Mother living with partner, smoker

Cigarette smoking was also associated with having a household member with a long-standing health problem or disability (p <0.005). It was also significantly related to the chances of a respondent pro-viding special care for someone in the family. While 5% of the never smokers reported providing special care, the proportion rose to 14% among the heavy smokers (p <0.005).

These differences in family health status are reflected in the mothers' assessments of their children's health. As would be predicated, heavy smokers were more likely to report that their baby weighed less than 2500 grams at birth (14%), a proportion that fell to 8% among ex-smokers and never smokers. This difference, however, was not statis-tically significant. But, as Figure 6.1 suggests, there were significant differences in the reported health status of the youngest child. While 61% of the mothers who had never smoked assessed their baby's health as excellent, less than half (45%) of the heavy smokers gave this positive assessment of their baby's health.

Figure 6.1   Youngest child's reported health status by smoking status (n=905)   (p<0.05)

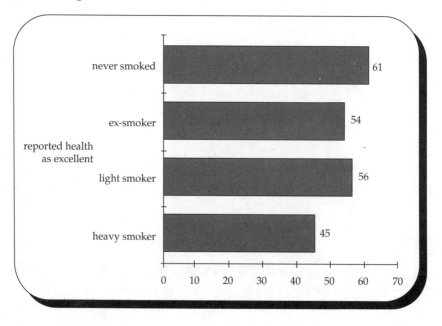

Reflecting these differences in their assessment of their baby's health, heavy smokers were more likely to report that their youngest child had health problems: 18% of heavy smokers compared with 9% of those who had never smoked (p <0.05). The mean number of symptoms reported for the youngest child was significantly higher in both smoking groups than in the other two groups (p <0.01) and the mean number of symptoms in the older children of heavy smokers was also higher than for the other three groups.

The link between cigarette smoking and additional caring responsibilities is confirmed in other ways. Figure 6.2 examines the associations between smoking status and lone motherhood. It suggests that the proportion of women who were caring for children alone was closely related to their smoking behaviour. The lowest proportion of mothers without partners was found among respondents who had never smoked (15%) and the highest proportion among mothers who were heavy smokers (32%).

Figure 6.2   The proportion of mothers living without a partner by smoking status   (n = 905)   (p <0.0001)

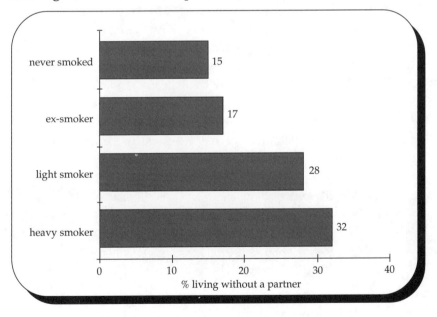

It's a problem bringing up the baby by myself. I've only been by myself for 9 weeks. My relationship with my fiancé broke down and I'm frightened that he will find out where I'm living now.

Single mother, smoker

I've been trying to get maintenance for the baby. My solicitor's advised me to settle out of court but I still don't get any money from him. And I've had all the hassles with the social — the rent etc — and trying to get them to organise the money. She (her baby) was born in October and they didn't sort out any money for me until December. It's a good job I've got a good family.

Single mother, smoker

6.4 Material circumstances

Being a smoker was not only associated with additional caring responsibilities. It was also associated with caring in circumstances of greater material disadvantage. A clear link between smoking status and material circumstances can be traced through the data on housing, income, employment and living standards. These dimensions are described briefly in turn. However, as the mothers' accounts of their problems make clear, difficulties in securing housing, income and employment are experienced as inter-linked rather than separate dimensions of their everyday lives.

The patterns of housing were closely related to smoking status, with non-smokers appearing to be more advantaged and smokers less advantaged within the housing market. Thus, as Figure 6.3 suggests, those who had never smoked were significantly more likely to be owner-occupiers. Conversely, those who had experienced an unstable housing situation were more likely to be heavy smokers. As Table 6.3 indicates, this group was significantly more likely to have moved five or more times in the last five years. Smoking status was also significantly related to the chances of having lived in bed and breakfast accommodation for more than a month ($p < 0.0001$).

My husband's been sick and out of work for 18 months. He managed to get a job here but no accommodation. We're renting but it's expensive and the tenancy finishes in December and we'll be homeless if we can't find anywhere else. We've no money for our own home and we'll be back in bed and breakfast again.

Mother living with partner, smoker

Before the baby was born, I was in bed and breakfast and I thought when she was born I was going to be put in a hostel with a young baby. I was under a lot of stress due to other things too, I was taking it out on my boyfriend.

Mother living with partner, smoker

I quarrelled with my mum when I got pregnant and had to move into a hostel. Since then, I've had the worry about finding somewhere to live and the worry about the new baby.

Single mother, smoker

Figure 6.3   Tenure and smoking status
(n=905)   (p <0.0001)

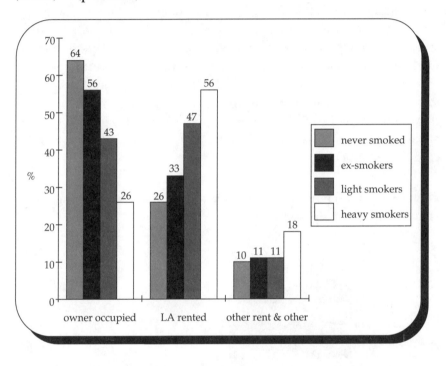

Reflecting the more disadvantaged housing position of the heavy smokers, it was mothers in this group who were particularly likely to report problems with their property. A large majority of the heavy smokers (76%) reported problems. In contrast, the majority (58%) of mothers who had never smoked reported no problems with their property (p <0.001). There was a clear relationship between smoking status and a range of housing problems, including damp and insufficient heating, insufficient play space, noise and lack of repairs. Among the heavy smokers, for example, 19% reported that their accommodation needed repair; the proportion among the never smokers was 9% (p <0.005). Among the heavy smokers, 29% noted that their home was insufficiently heated, a proportion which fell to 16% among the never-smokers (p <0.005).

Table 6.3:   **Changes of address and smoking status: proportion of mothers moving 5 or more times in the last 5 years   (n=905)   (p<0.0001)**

	%
Never smoked	3
Ex-smokers	4
Light smokers	4
Heavy smokers	18

Turning from housing to financial circumstances, Figure 6.4 indicates a strong association between smoking status and benefit status. Among those who had never smoked, one fifth (21%) were in households in receipt of income support. The proportion rose to one half (51%) among the respondents who were heavy smokers. This statistically-significant relationship remained when the range of benefits was extended to include unemployment benefit, invalidity and sickness benefits, disability and attendance allowances and family credit (p <0.0001).

Figure 6.4   Households in receipt of income support by smoking status   (n=905)   (p<0.0001)

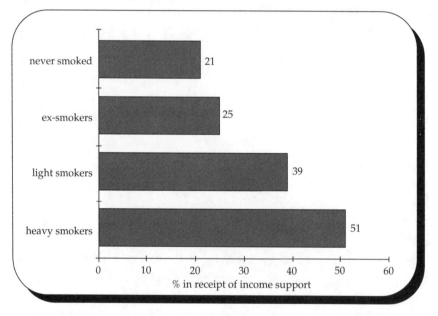

There were also differences in the employment status of partners. Among women living with a partner, smokers were much less likely to have a partner in employment. While 7% of the non-smokers had a partner who was not in paid employment, the proportion rose to 21%

among the heavy smokers (p <0.0001). A combined analysis relating to whether anyone in the household was in paid employment indicated that, among the heavy smokers, over 50% of their households had no-one in employment. Among respondents who had never smoked, the proportion was 21% (Figure 6.5).

> *He (partner) had an accident at work and broke his wrist. He has had metal pins inserted. It happened about Christmas and he is still out of work. He shared his house with his sister and her husband, so when I became pregnant, there wasn't enough room and we had to find somewhere else to live. We thought we might have to go into bed and breakfast. We got this house about a week before she (daughter) was born. We were quite lucky really.*
>
> *Mother living with partner, smoker*

Figure 6.5 Mothers living in a household with no-one in paid employment by smoking status   (n = 905)   (p<0.0001)

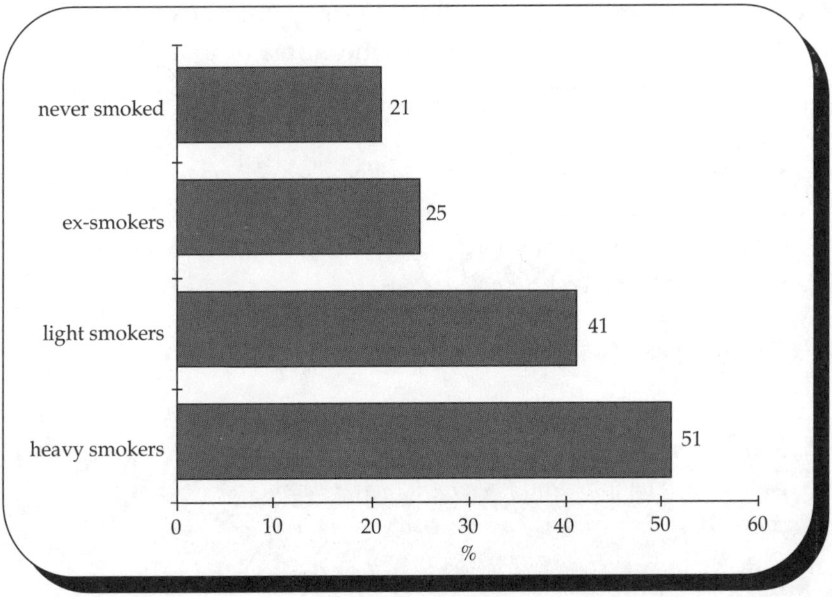

> *My husband is out of work and we always argue when he is offered a job and he won't take it because it's too low paid and he says he will lose things like family credit. I want him to go to work and get from under my feet.*
>
> *Mother living with partner, smoker*

In line with the differences in employment and benefit status, there was a clear gradient in the patterns of access to a car/van and a telephone. As Figure 6.6 indicates, mothers who had never smoked were significantly more likely to live in a household with a car/van and a telephone. Conversely, mothers who were light and heavy smokers were much more likely to be what one recent study calls 'communication and transport deprived' [1]. They were caring for a young family without a direct means of access to preventive and primary health care services. Yet, as noted in the previous section, it was smokers who were more likely to live with household members needing additional care and with children in poorer health.

Smoking status also exerted an influence on other measures of economic well-being. For example, the proportion of respondents reporting debts rose steadily from a low of 39% among never-smokers to a high of 53% among heavy smokers (p<0.01). Similar gradients emerged when respondents were asked about their current financial circumstances. The proportion of mothers reporting that their household financial situation was getting worse rose from 31% among the never-smokers to 42% among the heavy smokers. It should be noted that such assessments are likely to be more directly affected by expenditure on cigarettes than other measures of material circumstances considered in this section.

> Bills are a problem. The problem is really when the money situation gets you really depressed, you might go out and buy something like some nice beefburgers and that makes it worse We've got rent arrears of over a £1000, now every week the amount goes up.

> We've so many debts we don't know what to do.

> Fear of eviction is our biggest problem. It's still on-going. We have to go to court. If we can guarantee to pay they probably won't evict us. And the poll tax is a big problem. I received a letter saying they would take me to court as I hadn't paid it. I missed two payments.

> *Mothers living with a partner, smokers*

6.5 Smoking and disadvantage

The evidence from the study suggests that cigarette smoking is strongly associated with the material circumstances of mothers' lives. Mothers who smoke, and smoke heavily, are more likely to be caring in disadvantaged material circumstances than mothers who have given up smoking or who have never become regular smokers.

Figure 6.6 Proportion of mothers in the four smoking status groups living in households with a telephone and a car/van by smoking status (n = 905) (p<0.0001)

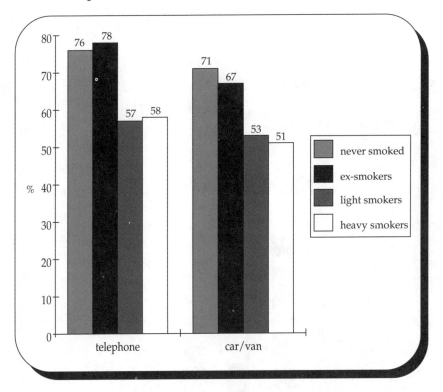

In order to examine the association between smoking and material disadvantage further, a composite measure of disadvantage was constructed. The variables included in this composite measure were ones which previous studies suggested were reliable indicators of disadvantage [2–4]. The variables are listed in Table 6.4.

Table 6.4: **Index of disadvantage**

No-one in the household employed

No car available

No telephone in the accommodation

Having debts

Bringing up children alone

Never had a full-time job

Having lived in bed and breakfast accommodation for more than a month

The patterns which emerged from this measure are plotted in Figure 6.7. They underline the relatively disadvantaged situation of most of the mothers in the study: only one in five (21%) was facing none of the problems included in the index. For the remainder, their scores ranged between 1 and 6; three in ten respondents (29%) had a score of three or more.

> I smoke more like if I've got bills coming in, I tend to get worried. I smoke when I'm worried. Like Christmas is coming and I'm not able to afford the things my children want.
>
> *Single mother, smoker*

Figure 6.7   Patterns of disadvantage within the sample   (n=905)

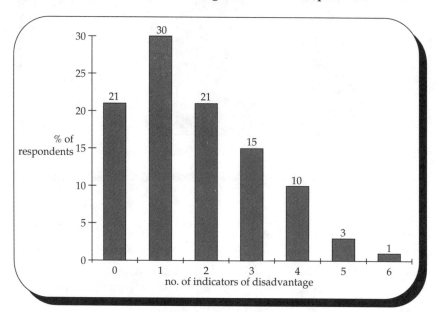

As Figure 6.7 underlines, the experience of disadvantage was one that framed the everyday lives of most of the mothers in the study. Within this disadvantaged group, smoking was strongly associated with greater levels of disadvantage. This association is captured in Figure 6.8. The figure defines multiple disadvantage as the experience of three or more dimensions of disadvantage and records the proportions of mothers in the four smoking status groups with scores at this level. The figure underlines the differences in the material circumstances of mothers in the four groups, confirming the sharp gradient of disadvantage apparent in the separate measures of living standards described in the previous section.

Figure 6.8   Multiple disadvantage and smoking status: proportion of mothers with 3 or more indicators of disadvantage (n=905)   (p<0.0001)

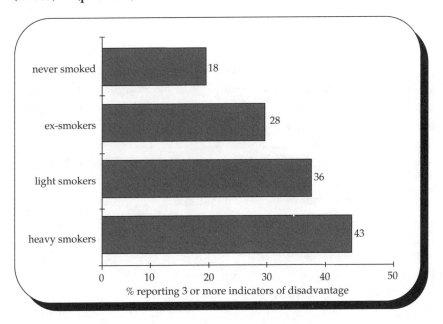

While living and caring in disadvantaged circumstances was strongly associated both with cigarette smoking and with tobacco consumption, not all cigarette smokers scored highly on the index of disadvantage. Around one in three (31%) of the smokers had one or no indicators of disadvantage. Analyses of this group of more advantaged smokers suggested no other differences between them and the other smokers in the sample. They were not different with respect to their family backgrounds or smoking careers or with respect to their current social or health circumstances. As a group who did not face the clustering of material disadvantages typically associated with smoking among working class mothers, they may represent a population which could be successfully targeted in health promotion programmes.

6.6   Summary

The design of the study meant that the mothers who took part shared a broadly similar domestic position and broadly similar socio-economic circumstances. Yet, sharp differences emerged among the mothers with respect to their caring responsibilities and their access to material resources. These differences were, in turn, strongly associated with smoking status. The findings relating to caring responsibilities and material resources point to a gradient of disadvantage which runs from the group of mothers who reported that they had never smoked through the ex-smokers and light smokers to the heavy smokers.

In relation to caring responsibilities, the smokers were more likely to be carrying an additional caring load. Cigarette smoking, and heavy smoking in particular, was associated with living in households with more children and with children and partners in poorer health. Heavy smoking was also associated with providing special care for a member of the household. Light and heavy smokers were more likely to be bringing up children as lone mothers than non-smokers.

In relation to material resources, the smokers were more likely to be caring in circumstances of greater material disadvantage. A clear gradient of disadvantage emerged with respect to a range of measures of living standards. These measures included the likelihood of mothers living in households dependent on benefits, living in rented accommodation, changing addresses frequently, not having access to a car/van and telephone and reporting problems with their property and in the physical environment of their neighbourhood.

This gradient of disadvantage emerged again in the composite measure of disadvantage, constructed to test further the association between smoking status and material circumstances. Heavy smokers were nearly two and a half times more likely than mothers who had never smoked to be caring for children in circumstances of multiple disadvantage.

Chapter 7

Social support and health resources

7.1 Introduction

The everyday lives of the mothers in the study were structured around their childcare responsibilities. Caring on a full-time basis for young children was an experience that smokers and non-smokers shared. However, the patterns described in chapter 6 suggest that the nature of mothers' caring responsibilities and the material contexts in which they carried them differed markedly by smoking status.

This chapter examines the associations between smoking status and mothers' social and health circumstances. Building on the analyses presented in chapter 6, it focuses on whether and how smoking status was linked to mothers' access to social support, to their health and health beliefs and to aspects of their health-related behaviour.

7.2 Social support and networks

Chapter 6 pointed to a strong association between smoking status and access to material resources. This strong association was not repeated in the patterns of social contact and support among mothers in the four smoking groups. There was no equivalent gradient of disadvantage in access to social resources.

The patterns of contact with parents were similar among the four smoking groups, with no significant differences between them. Nine in ten mothers in the four smoking status groups reported being close to their parents. The four smoking status groups did not differ significantly with respect to feeling close to their partners and, for respondents living with a partner, to members of their partner's family.

Similarly, there were no significant differences in the proportions of mothers in the different smoking status groups reporting that they had friends or neighbours to whom they felt very close or in the proportion reporting that a close friend or relative had died in the past year. Again, as Figures 7.1 and 7.2 summarise, the proportion reporting that they had someone to whom they felt very close and in whom they could confide about personal problems was similar across all four groups. Among respondents living with partners, patterns of confiding relationships also did not vary significantly by smoking status. When asked about their religious commitments, never smokers and ex-smokers were more likely to describe themselves as having a strong religious faith than light and heavy smokers (p <0.005).

Figure 7.1   Social intimacy and smoking status: proportion of mothers reporting having someone to whom they feel very close (n=905)

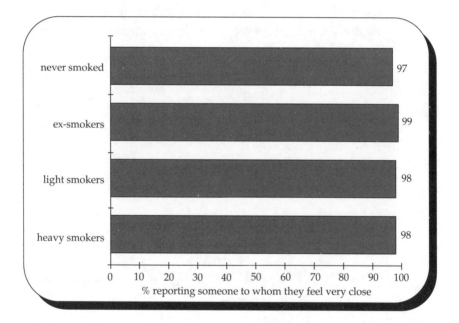

These measures of informal support suggest similarities rather than differences among the four groups of respondents. However, when a range of social support measures was combined to produce a general social support variable, smokers were less likely to be receiving such support than the two non-smoking groups (p <0.01). The measures were having a close friend/relative die, feeling close to relatives and friends, having someone to confide in and having a strong religious faith. This suggests that dimensions of informal support may mesh to provide a less supportive structure for the everyday lives of smokers than that enjoyed by the never and ex-smokers.

Figure 7.2   Social support and smoking status: proportion of mothers reporting having a confidant for personal problems   (n=905)

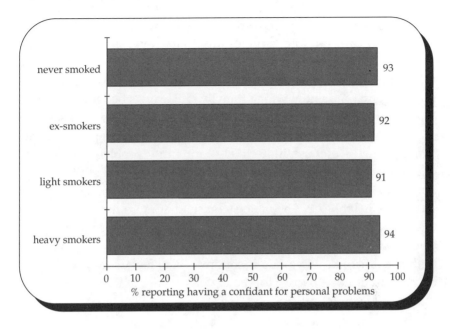

There is some further evidence to suggest that smokers felt less supported by and integrated into informal networks beyond the home. For example, they held less positive views about their neighbourhood. Light and heavy smokers were significantly less likely to report their neighbourhood as a good one for children to grow up in (p <0.0001). They were also significantly less likely to describe it as a friendly place to live or to say that they felt a sense of belonging to their neighbourhood. Table 7.1 summarises these differences.

Table 7.1:   **Mothers' feelings about their neighbourhood and smoking status: proportion of mothers reporting their neighbourhoods as friendly and ones to which they belonged   (n=905)**

	Feeling they belong % *(p <0.001)*	*Felt neighbourhood was friendly* % *(p <0.05)*
Never smoked	81	85
Ex-smoker	75	85
Light smoker	66	79
Heavy smoker	59	72

Mothers' perceptions of their neighbourhood are likely to be influenced by the material circumstances of their lives. As noted in chapter 6, smokers, and heavy smokers in particular, were more likely to have moved recently and moved often. They were less likely to have access to a car/van and a telephone than never and ex-smokers. These material differences in the living standards of mothers in the four smoking groups were reproduced in their assessment of the physical environment in which they lived. Heavy smokers were more likely than never smokers to report problems relating to their sense of security in their neighbourhood (vandalism, not feeling safe on the streets). They were also more likely to identify problems relating to the safety of their children outside the home (dogs, lack of play space, dangerous roads). The differences associated with smoking status are indicated in Table 7.2. The table suggests that more than a quarter of the heavy smokers reported problems relating to one or more aspects of personal security and more than half identified problems relating to the health and safety of their children. Such factors may well act as a brake on, if not a barrier to, the development of close relationships within their communities.

Table 7.2: **Problems with the neighbourhood: never smokers and heavy smokers compared (n=905)**

	Never Smoked %	Heavy Smokers %
Don't feel safe on street*	17	26
Vandals**	18	28
Dogs***	35	53
Lack of play space*	39	51

*   p <0.05

**   p <0.01

***   p <0.005

7.3   Health status

It was noted in Chapter 6 that smokers were likely to be caring for more children than non-smokers. They were also more likely to be caring for children, and other family members, who had health problems and who needed help with everyday care tasks. Smokers thus faced additional demands on their personal health resources. While needing more in the way of physical and emotional stamina, it was smokers, and heavy smokers in particular, who were more likely to report that their physical and emotional health was poor.

Figure 7.3 points to a close association between self-rated health and smoking status, with heavy smokers less likely to report excellent health, and more likely to report poor health.

Figure 7.3 Self-assessed health and smoking status: proportion of mothers assessing their health as fair or poor   (n=905)   (p <0.0001)

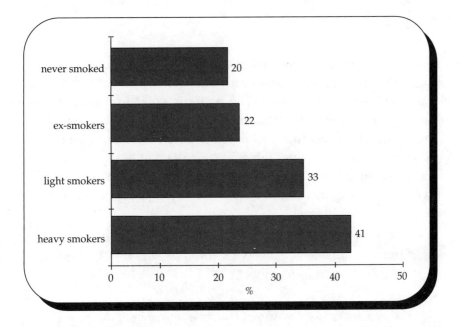

There was a similar gradient in symptom-reporting. As Table 7.3 indicates, smokers were more likely to report smoking-related symptoms like coughs and breathlessness in the two weeks prior to the interview. They were also more likely to report headaches and feeling constantly tired. Reflecting these different patterns of symptoms, never-smokers reported the lowest mean numbers of symptoms. Heavy smokers reported a higher mean number of symptoms than ex-smokers and those who had never smoked (p <0.01). However, while the findings point to poorer health status among light and heavy smokers, these groups were not more likely to report long-standing health problems.

Table 7.3: **Symptoms reported during the previous two weeks by smoking status   (n=905)**

	Constant Tiredness*	Persistent Cough**	Breathlessness**
	%	%	%
Never smoked	50	7	6
Ex-smokers	44	8	6
Light smokers	58	14	14
Heavy smokers	63	24	20

* $p < 0.01$

** $p < 0.001$

Turning to measures which more explicitly address mothers' psycho-social well-being, clear differences are again apparent between the four smoking status groups. The patterns point to poorer psycho-social health among the smokers, with the ex-smokers emerging as the group least likely to report psychological difficulties on a number of measures of well-being. Table 7.4 suggests that nearly half (46%) of the heavy smokers identified feeling alone and isolated as a problem that they had experienced in the past year. The proportion among the ex-smokers was 29%.

> *Times or situations mothers identified as ones in which they were very likely to want to smoke*

> *When I'm depressed or bored. That's the only thing I can do – smoke. I just sit down with a cigarette and watch TV. When me and my husband have had a row. Because I'm upset: I smoke to cheer me up.*

> *Mother living with partner, smoker*

> *When the kids are all in bed and the TV has nothing on and I've got no-one to talk to and I just smoke out of boredom.*

> *Single mother, smoker*

> *When I first wake up and feel depressed. When I'm tired and worn out or when the children get a bit stroppy. When I'm violently mad and about to throttle them.*

> *Mother living with partner, smoker*

Table 7.4: **Proportion of mothers reporting isolation as a problem in the last year by smoking status   (n=905)   (p<0.005)**

	%
Never smoked	36
Ex-smokers	29
Light smokers	44
Heavy smokers	46

The pattern of scores from the General Health Questionnaire paints a similar picture. The proportion of women with a score of three or more (the threshold for possible psychiatric symptoms) was at its highest among the heavy smoking group and at its lowest among the ex-smokers (Figure 7.4). While 46% of heavy smokers recorded scores of three or more on the GHQ-12, 26% of the ex-smokers were on or above this threshold. The ex-smokers had the lowest and heavy smokers had the highest mean scores (Table 7.5).

Figure 7.4   Proportion of mothers scoring three or more on the GHQ-12 by smoking status   (n=899)   (p <0.005)

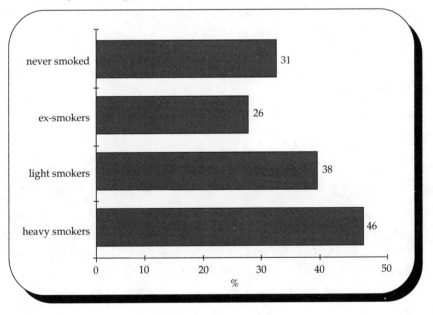

As the mothers' accounts make clear, emotional and physical health problems were often interwoven, and were reinforced by concerns about their personal and material circumstances.

We split up for a while, about 6 weeks. We weren't getting along and that really worried me, because of the thought of how I could look after a baby and work. Then I got the result of my cervical smear. I lost weight and was down to 6 stone after the baby was born, due to the worrying about it.

I've had major problems. I had a severe asthma attack which I was hospitalised for 10 days. Also, my baby's severe asthma attack, he was in hospital for 2 days. And the shortage of money.

I'm under strain because of his possessiveness, jealousy. He thinks he owns me. He cross-questions me all the time if I'm more than 5 minutes at the shop. I sometimes feel I'd like to leave. He carries on accusing me of having it off with someone else during the day. I've never been able to tell anyone this before as all my friends are his family, but it really does get me down.

I've been worrying a lot about finding somewhere to live. The hostel was like a prison. Then my partner lost his job after I had the baby and for a week or two we had no money at all.

Mothers living with a partner, smokers

Table 7.5: **Mean GHQ-12 scores by smoking status**
(n=899)   (for heavy smokers, p<0.025)

	Mean Score	*Standard Error*	*Number*
Never smoked	2.0136	.1500	295
Ex-smokers	1.8240	.2452	125
Light smokers	2.3560	.1605	309
Heavy smokers	2.9615	.2470	156

While the mean scores on the GHQ-12 pointed to better psycho-social health among the ex-smokers, it was the group of women who had never smoked who were most likely to feel that they had choice and control over their life. The proportion of those feeling that they exercised choice and control declined steadily from 81% among the never smokers to 70% among the heavy smokers (p <0.05). As with their assessments of their health, respondents' views on questions of choice and control highlighted the close connections between mothers' emotional well-being and the circumstances in which they were caring for children.

Why do you feel you do not have choice and control over the way your life is turning out?

Because I don't have the choices. It's usually financial reasons. Most other problems I can sort out. Like we can find baby sitters but not the fees. I wanted to go back to college after the baby was born but we couldn't afford the baby minder. It's purely money, that's all.

Mother with partner, smoker

I was meant to be with her dad, but he left me when she was one day old.

Single mother, non-smoker

Everything I want to do doesn't go right. I'd like to go on holiday but I never have the chance. It's always the financial part that stop us. There is a lot of things you can't control. And you can't do things without money.

Mother with partner, smoker

7.4   Health beliefs

There were no significant differences among the four smoking status groups in relation to beliefs about what determines health. A similar proportion of mothers in the four groups thought that health was primarily affected by things you do. The majority of mothers in the four smoking status groups recognised that lung cancer, bronchitis and heart disease were more common among smokers than non-smokers (Table 7.6). The majority also recognised the increased risks of chesty coughs and wheezes which passive smoking brought for children (Table 7.7). Within these patterns, heavy smokers were less likely to link smoking-related conditions to smoking. Conversely, non-smokers appeared to be more likely to identify a link between non-smoking related conditions and smoking.

Current smokers were asked if they felt that smoking was a hard habit to break. Heavy smokers were significantly more likely to view smoking as a habit that was hard to break than light smokers ($p < 0.0001$).

Table 7.6: **Diseases thought to be more common in smokers by smoking status   (n = 905)**

	Never Smoked %	Ex-smokers %	Light Smokers %	Heavy Smokers %
Lung Cancer**	95	93	93	83
Bronchitis*	94	92	90	83
Heart Disease**	82	80	73	68
Bad Circulation**	58	64	50	48
Breast Cancer (ns)	47	53	47	41
Diabetes***	13	6	6	4
Arthritis*	7	5	7	5

*	$p < 0.05$
**	$p < 0.01$
***	$p < 0.001$
ns	not significant

Table 7.7: **Diseases thought to be more common in children who live with smokers by smoking status   (n = 905)**

	Never Smoked %	Ex-smoker %	Light Smoker %	Heavy Smoker %
Chesty cough***	88	91	80	74
Wheeze***	79	85	69	64
Infections***	46	49	31	27
Skin problems***	21	17	10	6
Earache***	9	15	6	3
Bedwetting (ns)	2	2	1	1

***	$p < 0.001$
ns	not significant

7.5   Health-related behaviour

Cigarette smoking among women is associated with a cluster of other health-related behaviours, including tea and coffee consumption, alcohol consumption, food intake and infant feeding practices [1–4]. These associations were confirmed in the study.

Alcohol consumption: previous research has suggested that cigarette smoking and alcohol consumption among women have a different social profile. While female smokers are more likely to be younger and from lower socio-economic groups, the typical female drinker is more likely to be older and from the higher socio-economic groups [2–4]. National data suggest that 80% of mothers in social class V drink alcohol compared with 90% of mothers in social class I [2].

Reflecting the class background of the mothers in the study, the levels of reported alcohol consumption were low among all smoking status groups, with between 23% (ex-smokers) and 33% (heavy smokers) reporting that they never drank alcohol. Among those who reported that they sometimes drank, over 75% of the mothers in all four groups said that they drank little or hardly at all. However, among those reporting that they sometimes drank, heavy smokers were more likely to report moderate drinking or drinking quite a lot (p <0.05). They were also more likely to report that their parents drank regularly when the respondents were children (p <0.01). There were no differences between the groups in relation to whether their close friends drank regularly. Psycholog

Diet: the inverse relationship between tobacco smoking and body weight has been noted for over a century [5]. Studies have recorded that smokers weigh less than non-smokers and put on weight after stopping smoking [6]. Staying slim is one of the perceived benefits of smoking among school-aged girls and young women [7, 8]. As noted in chapter 5, putting on weight was one of the factors cited by smokers in the study to explain why their last attempt at quitting had been unsuccessful.

In line with earlier studies, the evidence from the survey points to an association between reported smoking status and reported food intake. Smokers, both light and heavy, were less likely to report that they were eating too much food than never smokers and ex-smokers (Table 7.8). They were more likely to report that they were not eating enough. Confirming this pattern of association between smoking and low food intake, significantly more never-smokers and ex-smokers PTO reported that they were trying to lose weight.

Table 7.8:   **Diet and smoking status (n = 905)**

	Eating too much %	Trying to lose weight %
	(p <0.005)	(p <0.001)
Never smoked	34	50
Ex-smokers	42	50
Light smokers	26	34
Heavy smokers	24	33

Tea and coffee consumption: in line with other studies, the survey points to a positive association between tobacco and tea/coffee consumption among working class mothers [1]. Rather than tea and coffee serving as a substitute for cigarettes among the non-smokers, it was the smokers, and particularly the high smokers, who reported the highest consumption of tea and coffee. Approaching four times as many heavy smokers and twice as many light smokers said that they drank more than six cups of tea or coffee a day as never-smokers (Figure 7.5).

Maternal health behaviour: smoking status was associated with the small range of indicators of maternal health behaviour measured in the study. Ex-smokers and women who had never smoked were significantly more likely to report that they had breast fed their baby after s/he was born. As Figure 7.6 indicates, a third of the light and heavy smokers breast fed their babies, compared with over half of the never smokers and ex-smokers. Smoking status was also related to attendance for a post-natal check up. Of the 76 women (8% of the total sample) who said that they had not had a post-natal check up, 59 were smokers: almost four times as many smokers as non-smokers said that they had not had a check up (p <0.0001).

The patterns of maternal health behaviour, including breast feeding and clinic attendance, may well be related to the material circumstances of respondents' lives. Breast feeding patterns may reflect the poor housing and financial circumstances associated with light and

Figure 7.5 Tea and coffee drinking by smoking status: proportion of mothers drinking more than six cups a day   (n=905)   (p <0.001)

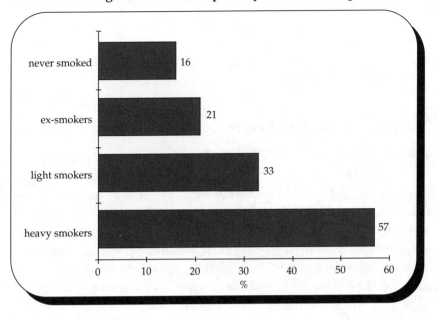

heavy smoking, while the patterns of attendance for a post-natal check-up may reflect the more frequent changes of address and more restricted access to a car/van found among the high smokers.

Figure 7.6 Breast feeding and smoking status: proportion of mothers breast feeding their baby after s/he was born   (n=905)   (p <0.001)

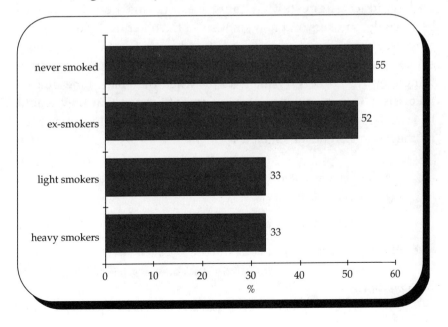

Contraceptive behaviour also varied with smoking status. It was light smokers who were most likely to be taking the pill (52%), with heavy smokers least likely to be pill-users (37%) (p <0.01). There were no significant differences in the proportions of mothers reporting that they were taking or had taken tranquillisers. However, it should be noted that the proportion in the sample as a whole who reported tranquilliser use was low.

7.6   Smoking and alternative coping strategies

The evidence presented in chapters 5, 6 and 7 suggests that cigarette smoking may both reflect, and be a way of coping with, ongoing material difficulties and health problems. The survey included questions which tapped into this link between cigarette smoking and mothers' daily lives. As reported in chapter 5, current smokers were asked if there were particular times of the day or particular situations in which they were very likely to smoke. The majority of smokers said that there were, with 90% identifying having time to oneself and feeling on edge as situations in which they would be likely to smoke (see section 5.4). The survey also asked mothers about a range of alternative activities, including the consumption of coffee, tea and alcohol, to which they might turn in these everyday situations. Were non-smokers using these alternative coping strategies in circumstances where smokers were turning to cigarettes?

The evidence suggests that there were no marked differences between the smokers and non-smokers in the other lifestyle measures they used when they had time to themselves or felt on edge. A very similar proportion identified having a cup of tea or coffee as something they would be very likely to do when they had some time to themselves. Among the heavy smokers, 75% stated that they would be very likely to have a cup of coffee or tea: the proportion among the mothers who had never smoked was 78%.

> I smoke after a meal and when I have a drink of tea or if something got me angry. And boredom as well.

> I smoke when I'm having a cup of tea. After a meal. During this interview.

> After a meal when I get a break, I really enjoy one. That's the only one I really enjoy. The others are habit. I also smoke when I'm under a lot of pressure.

> Mothers living with a partner, smokers

The patterns of response to the questions about feeling on edge again failed to identify alternatives to cigarettes among the non-smokers. Among the heavy smokers, over 70% said that they would be very likely to smoke when they were feeling on edge, typically combining a cigarette with a cup of coffee. For a small minority (8%), cigarettes were combined with an alcoholic drink. Among the never-smokers, the largest group (59%) identified none of the alternatives (tea, coffee and alcoholic drink) as ones they would be very likely to have when feeling on edge. Just under a third (31%) reported that they would be very likely to have a cup of tea/coffee; 10% said that they would be very likely to have an alcoholic drink.

The range of potential strategies covered in the survey is clearly limited. There may well be other strategies that the non-smoking mothers had developed to cope with the demands of young children while remaining with them. However, there appears to be little evidence to suggest that non-smokers were relying on tea/coffee or alcoholic drinks in situations where smokers were turning to cigarettes.

7.7 Summary

The chapter has built on the analysis of social and material factors associated with smoking status provided in chapter 6 by examining the links between smoking and mothers' social and health resources. Like chapter 6, it divided the sample into four smoking status groups: those who had never smoked, ex-smokers, light smokers and heavy smokers.

The evidence summarised in the chapter suggests that, while smoking was associated with restricted access to material resources, it was not associated with restricted access to family and friendship networks. Mothers did not differ significantly in terms of their access to close and confiding relationships with family, partners and friends. Looking more broadly at mothers' social circumstances, however, smokers appeared to be less well supported by and integrated into the neighbourhoods in which they lived. Their neighbourhoods were experienced as less friendly and more dangerous ones in which to bring up children.

Smoking status was more clearly linked to health status. Smokers, and heavy smokers in particular, were more likely to be caring when their own physical and emotional health was poor. Light and heavy smokers were less likely to rate their health positively than non-smokers and were more likely to experiences symptoms of physical ill-health. Their emotional health, as measured by the General Health Questionnaire, also tended to be poorer. Against this backdrop of poorer physical and psycho-social health, cigarette smoking was linked to feeling on edge and having time for oneself. There was little evidence to suggest that non-smokers had developed alternative strategies to deal with the two situations in which smokers were very likely to smoke. The evidence, instead, suggests that never-smokers and ex-smokers were protected from the circumstances and experiences which sustained cigarette smoking and made it hard for the current smokers to give up.

Chapter 8

Conclusions and implications

8.1 Conclusions

The health professions are seeking to meet government targets for smoking cessation against trends which are tying cigarettes smoking more closely to dimensions of social disadvantage. As smoking prevalence in Britain has fallen, the proportion of women in the smoking population has risen [1]. Declining prevalence has been associated, too, with the emergence of a sharp socio-economic gradient in cigarette smoking [1]. While linked to class disadvantage, women's smoking is not associated with minority ethnic status: smoking remains a habit acquired and sustained by White women.

These gender and class trends have emerged across a period in which health policies have increasingly emphasised the health-risks of smoking. Anti-smoking education has been incorporated into the mainstream of health promotion and primary health care, figuring centrally in national campaigns, local initiatives and patient education in the surgery, clinic and community [2–5]. The investment in health education is reflected in high levels of public awareness of the dangers of smoking [6]. Public knowledge about these dangers has risen sharply since the 1960s, with knowledge and beliefs about smoking varying little either by gender or by social class [7, 8]. The vast majority of those in non-manual and manual socio-economic groups recognise the general and specific health-risks of smoking [6, 8, 9]. However, knowledge and beliefs have been unevenly translated into behaviour. It is among men and those in non-manual households that behaviour has changed most markedly. In contrast, among women and among those in manual households, the rates of smoking acquisition and smoking cessation have changed more slowly [1]. The challenge for health promotion is to address the gender and class factors which sustain cigarette smoking in the face of knowledge of its health-damaging consequences.

This book has addressed some of these factors. It has focused on a group within Britain's smoking population where both gender roles and socio-economic circumstances have been identified as important barriers to behavioural change. It has focused on White women caring for young children in households where the head of household is either outside the labour market or is employed in a manual occupation within it. The broad associations between gender, class and cigarette smoking uncovered in national surveys were confirmed in this more tightly-focused sample. They were repeated in ways that shed an important light on what it is about being a woman and being working class that links these dimensions of identity to smoking behaviour.

The survey's findings suggest that smokers are drawn disproportionately from those who are disadvantaged within their gender and class groups. The mothers who smoked faced additional demands in relation to their gender responsibilities and additional difficulties in relation to their material circumstances. Looking at their lives as the mothers of young children, the heavy smoking group were caring for more children and for children in poorer health. They were also more likely to be caring alone and to be carrying extra responsibilities for the care of family members who needed help with health-tasks. Looking at their lives as mothers in a working class household, a higher proportion of smokers were dependent on benefit-level incomes and reported that they were caring on less than they needed to meet the basic necessities of their families. They were less likely to live in a neighbourhood which they regarded as a good one in which to bring up children. Demands and disadvantages also tracked their way into mothers' perceptions of their health. Smokers were more likely to report poor psycho-social health, with nearly half the heavy smokers scoring 3 or more on the General Health Questionnaire.

Drawing conclusions from the study, it suggests that caring for more and living on less is part of the cluster of experiences that sustains smoking among White working class women. Caring for more and living on less provides the context in which relatively few mothers attempt, and fewer succeed at, giving up smoking. Highlighting factors associated with high smoking prevalence and low smoking cessation rates, the survey's findings go some way to answering questions about the changing social distribution of cigarette smoking in Britain. The findings suggest that smoking among women in working class households is linked, in direct and systematic ways, to the caring responsibilities and the material circumstances which shape their everyday lives.

8.2 Implications for health promotion and smoking cessation programmes

The implications of the study for health promotion policies and smoking cessation strategies need to be cautiously drawn. As noted in chapter 4, the survey was located in one region of England and based on a non-random sample with a relatively high non-response rate. It selected its sample on the basis of occupational information held on maternity records and relied on self-reported data. Its findings therefore raise rather than resolve questions about the current direction of policies designed to achieve a reduction in smoking prevalence among women. The findings raise particular questions about the timing and orientation of health promotion policies directed at working class women.

Health Prom programmes aim to reduce smoking prevalence in women

Firstly, on the question of timing, anti-smoking campaigns and programmes have been directed towards expectant mothers and mothers with young children. Pregnancy and early motherhood have been seen as offering unrivalled opportunities for education and intervention [10]. However, the evidence from mothers in the study suggests that the months before and after birth provide little opportunity to initiate and sustain the changes in smoking behaviour sought by health professionals.

In contrast to the mothers who had never smoked or who succeeded in giving up smoking, the smokers tended to be caring in circumstances which constrained rather than supported lifestyle change. The mothers who smoked, and particularly those who smoked heavily, were likely to be carrying additional caring responsibilities in poorer health and in more disadvantaged material circumstances. Cigarette smoking was a habit to which mothers turned when the demands of their everyday lives left them feeling on edge.

For a significant number of the smokers, it is not only their smoking behaviour that was likely to be a focus of professional intervention. Other aspects of their health behaviour (like their clinic attendance) and their childcare practices (like their patterns of infant feeding) may have also brought them to the attention of health workers. The smokers in the study were also more likely than the non-smokers to be claimants, to be in debt, to be council tenants and to be lone mothers, dimensions which again are likely to increase their interaction with welfare agencies.

The pattern of difficulties and disadvantages faced by this group of smokers suggests that their adaptive capacity may already be taxed to the limit. In such circumstances, the scope for health-related behavioural change may be limited [11]. The patterns of smoking cessation confirm the conclusion that many mothers found it hard to initiate and sustain changes in smoking behaviour during the period targeted by health professionals. Only four in ten of the smokers had tried to give up smoking during their last pregnancy and the six months after birth. Of the mothers who reported themselves to be cigarette smokers at the start of their pregnancy, 15 months earlier, over 90% were still smokers by the time their baby was six months old.

All this points to the importance of broadening the timescale for anti-smoking programmes aimed at working class women. It points to the fact that, while many smokers manage to reduce their consumption in pregnancy, smoking cessation during and after pregnancy may remain an unattainable goal for the majority of working class mothers.

Why are you smoking fewer cigarettes now than when you were pregnant?

Because the pressures are less than before. Now I've had the baby, things are better. Because I was really unhappy when I was pregnant. Now I'm getting on better. It's very tiring when you have two small children but now I can get out more, I am coping much better and the stress is less.

Single mother, smoker

I was under a lot of stress. I was going through a custody case, trying to get my older son back.

Single mother, smoker

Because it was my sixth pregnancy — it was the stress really. I tried not to let it go above 5 a day.

Mother living with partner, smoker

It started when I finished work. You don't want to keep eating. It's a sort of pressure to smoke. When I was off work before she was born, I always used to meet up town with my mate and her grandmother and her mother

and I always smoked one after the other — I just got into the same habit.
You don't realise until you count what you've got through, how many
you've had.

Mother living with partner, smoker

The survey raises a second set of issues, about the orientation of health promotion policies designed to help women give up smoking. It confirms the findings of other studies that there is no straightforward connection between knowledge and behaviour: women knew about the health-risks of smoking but continued to smoke despite this knowledge. The crucial connections lay, instead, in women's material and social circumstances. It was how women lived rather than what they knew which was the stronger predictor of their smoking status. The issue of how working class women live emerges as a major and urgent issue for health promotion policy and practice.

One way of recognising the link between smoking and women's everyday lives would be to target smoking education and professional support at more advantaged groups of mothers within and beyond working class communities. The study suggests that, while smoking is closely linked to disadvantage among working class women, there are women who are not as severely disadvantaged as other groups of smokers. In the study, one in ten of the heavy smokers did not report any of the indicators which formed the index of disadvantage and a further two in ten had a score of one. Analysis of this group suggests that, in other respects, they were similar to other smokers. They were not, for example, more disadvantaged in terms of their caring responsibilities, their social networks or their health and personal resources. The findings on the patterns of ex-smokers suggest that greater material advantage may be a factor which supports smoking cessation. This group of more advantaged smokers may thus be more likely to give up smoking than mothers caring for children in poorer material circumstances.

While targeting health promotion resources at more advantaged mothers may provide one way forward for anti-smoking programmes, it avoids rather than addresses the increasingly strong connection between smoking and disadvantage among women. The study's findings point to the need to broaden the base of health promotion and tobacco cessation policies, to include interventions which act directly on the circumstances of women's lives. They point, in other words, to programmes concerned with how women live as well as what they know. Strategies to alleviate the factors associated with high smoking prevalence and high tobacco consumption could become an explicit part of health promotion policy, at national and local level. Interventions which help reduce the burdens of heavy caring responsibilities and improve women's material circumstances may lift the barriers which prevent at least some working class women from trying, and trying again, to give up smoking.

> *Why are you smoking more cigarettes now than when you were pregnant?*
>
> *Because I spend all day at home. When I was at work, I could only smoke in the dinner hour but now I have all day at home so I tend to smoke more. It's just boredom. When you watch telly, you just tend to light one up.*
>
> > *Mother living with partner, smoker*
>
> *I don't know. I've had a lot of trouble with my husband and we've split up. My daughter has been upset because my husband wanted her to live with him and she didn't want to go. I was upset because she was upset.*
>
> > *Single mother, smoker*
>
> *I don't know. I think I need more these days. When I lose my temper, I just sit down and have a cigarette. It seems to calm me down. It's when they're all crying and that. After I've sorted them all out, I just sit down and relax.*
>
> > *Mother living with partner, smoker*
>
> *Don't know. I think it's because I'm stuck in the flat more. I don't see anyone from day to day. When my husband comes in at night, I cut down again straight away. So it's probably boredom and sitting here all on my own.*
>
> > *Mother living with partner, smoker*

Initiatives which address the context of mothers' lives as well as the content of their health-related behaviour have achieved impressive results. For example, the Newcastle Community Midwifery Care Project provided enhanced midwifery care to expectant mothers at home and increased access to other welfare services. It offered ongoing professional support around the adoption of health-promoting lifestyles. One in two (47%) of the mothers in households where the head of household was unemployed either stopped smoking or reduced their consumption. Among mothers in the control group, only one in four (25%) of those in unemployed households cut down or quit smoking [12]. A crucial element in the success of the project appeared to the way professional support encouraged a sense of pride and achievement in the difficult task of making lifestyle changes.

Part of the Newcastle project's success may lie in its effect on mothers' confidence about their ability to affect changes in their lives. Confidence about oneself and optimism about one's future have been identified as important factors in smoking cessation. People give up smoking because they see their lives and identities as non-smokers as giving them more of what they want and less of what they fear [13]. Sensitively-designed professional intervention can not only bring about improvements in self-esteem, it can also bring about improvements in the circumstances of mothers' lives. Studies suggest that such improvements can be a trigger to changes in health-related behaviour. Both major life-events and relatively small-scale changes can prompt a reconsideration of a previously-routine habit, encouraging individuals to take the initiative in adopting more health-promoting lifestyles [14, 15].

The development and dissemination of approaches to smoking cessation which are sensitive to the everyday lives of working class women has been the focus of an Information Pack based on the study of working class mothers [16-18]. The Information Pack provides suggestions for multi-agency and individual practice that can help to lift some of the material and emotional pressures that work against smoking cessation. The Pack identifies ways in which health care professionals can support mothers in reducing the stress that can result from heavy caring responsibilities, disadvantaged material circumstances and poor personal health.

The Pack has been disseminated to health care professionals, for individual staff development and for group training. Health visitors, practice nurses, midwives, general practitioners and primary health care facilitators have all been major recipients. With 8,000 copies distributed, the evidence suggests that the health promotion community is committed to addressing rather than avoiding the links between smoking and disadvantage in women s lives. With their sights set on *The Health of the Nation* targets, many health care workers are clearly already committed to working alongside mothers, helping them to find ways of easing the pressures which make 'life a drag'.

References

Introduction

1. Royal College of Physicians of London (1983) *Health or Smoking*, follow-up report of the Royal College of Physicians, London: Pitmans Publishing.

2. Peto R, Lopez A D, Boreham J, Thun M and Heath C (1992) 'Mortality from tobacco in developed countries: indirect estimation from national vital statistics', *The Lancet*, 339: 1268–78.

3. Chief Medical Officer of Health (1989) *On the State of the Public Health for the Year 1988*, London: HMSO.

4. Royal College of Physicians (1992) *Smoking and the Young*, a report of a working party of the Royal College of Physicians, London: Royal College of Physicians.

5. Waldron I (1991) 'Patterns and causes of gender differences in smoking', *Social Science and Medicine*, 32, 9: 989–1005.

6. Wald N, Kiryluk S, Darby S, Doll R, Pike M, and Peto R (1988) *UK Smoking Statistics*, Oxford: Oxford University Press.

7. Office of Population Censuses and Surveys (1992) *General Household Survey 1990*, London: HMSO.

8. Secretary of State for Health (1992) *The Health of the Nation: A Strategy for Health in England*, London: HMSO.

9. Madeley R J, Gillies P A, Power F L and Symonds E M (1989) 'Nottingham Mothers Stop Smoking Project – baseline survey of smoking in pregnancy', *Community Medicine*, 11, 2: 124–30.

10. Waterson E J, and Murray-Lyon I M (1989) 'Drinking and smoking patterns amongst women attending an antenatal clinic – II. during pregnancy', *Alcohol and Alcoholism*, 24, 2: 163–73.

11. White A, Freeth S and O'Brien M, (1992) *Infant Feeding 1990*, London: HMSO.

12. Barker M E, McClean S I, McKenna P G, Reid N G, Strain J J, Thompson K A, Williamson A P and Wright M E (1989) *Diet, Lifestyle and Health in Northern Ireland*, Coleraine: Centre for Applied Health Studies, University of Ulster.

13. Blaxter M (1990) *Health and Lifestyles*, London: Routledge.

14. Graham H (1987) 'Women's smoking and family health', *Social Science and Medicine*, 25: 47–56.

15. Green G, MacIntyre S, West P and Ecob R (1990) 'Do children of lone parents smoke more because their mothers do?' *British Journal of Addiction*, 85: 1497–1500.

16. Marsh A and Matheson J (1983) *Smoking Attitudes and Behaviour*, London: HMSO.

17. Goddard, E (1990) *Why Children Start Smoking*, London: HMSO.

18. Ben-Shlamo I, Sheiham A and Marmot M (1991) 'Smoking and health' in Jowell R, Brook L and Taylor B (eds) *British Social Attitudes: the 8th Report*, Aldershot: Barmouth Publishing Company.

Chapter 1

1. Todd G F (1978) 'Cigarette consumption per adult of each sex in various countries', *Journal of Epidemiology and Community Health*, 32: 289–293.

2. Jackson R and Beaglehole R (1985) 'Secular trends in under-reporting of cigarette consumption', *American Journal of Epidemiology*, 122: 341–44.

3. Wald N, Kiryluk S, Darby S, Doll R, Pike M and Peto R (1988) *UK Smoking Statistics*, Oxford: Oxford University Press.

4. Pierce J P (1989) 'International comparisons in trends in cigarette smoking prevalence', *AJPH*, 79,2: 152–7.

5. Kozlowski L T and Heatherton T F (1990) 'Self-report issues in cigarette smoking: state of the art and future directions', *Behavioural Assessment*, 12: 53–75.

6. Chollat-Traquet C (1992) *Women and Tobacco*, Geneva: WHO.

7. Ernster V (1985) 'Mixed messages for women: a social history of cigarette smoking and advertising', *New York State Journal of Medicine*, July: 335–40.

8. Sullivan M (1927) *Our Times: The United States 1900–1925*, vol 2, New York: Charles Scribner's Sons.

9. Jacobson B (1986) *Beating the Ladykillers*, London: Pluto Press.

10. Dale E (1935) *The Content of Motion Pictures*, New York: The MacMillan Company.

11. McKennell A C and Thomas R K (1967) *Adults' and Adolescents' Smoking Habits and Attitudes*, London: HMSO.

12. Harrison, T (1976) *Living Through the Blitz*, London: Collins.

13. Calder, A and Sheridan, D (eds) (1984) *Speak For Yourself: A Mass Observation Anthology. 1937–49*, London: Jonathan Cape.

14. Sheridan, D (ed) (1990) *Wartime Women: A Mass Observation Anthology*, London: Mandarin.

15. Office of Population Censuses and Surveys (1992) *General Household Survey 1990*, London: OPCS.

Chapter 2

1. Wald N, Kiryluk S, Darby S, Doll R, Pike M and Peto R (1988) *UK Smoking Statistics*, Oxford: Oxford University Press.

2. Office of Population Censuses and Surveys (1992) *General Household Survey 1990*, London: OPCS.

3. Chollat-Traquet C (1992) *Women and Tobacco*, Geneva: WHO.

4. Fiore M C, Novotny T E, Pierce J P, Hatziandreu E J, Patel K M and Davis R M (1989) 'Trends in cigarette smoking in the United States', *JAMA*, 261, 1: 49-55.

5. Hay D R and Foster F H (1984) 'Intercensal trends in cigarette smoking in New Zealand I: age, sex and ethnic status', *New Zealand Medical Journal*, 97, 755: 283–85.

6. Ritchie J (1990) 'Women and smoking: a lethal deception', *Women's Studies International Forum*, 13, 3: 201–8.

7. Haglund M (1988) 'Development trends in smoking among women in Sweden: an analysis', in Aoki M (ed) *Smoking and Health*, Stockholm: Elsevier Science Publishers.

8. Rahkonen O, Berg M A and Puska P (1992) 'The development of smoking in Finland from 1978 to 1990', *British Journal of Addiction*, 87: 103–110.

9. Jarvis M and Johnson P (1988) 'Cigar and pipe smoking in Britain: implications for smoking prevalence and cessation', *British Journal of Addiction*, 83: 323–30.

10. Jarvis M (1984) 'Gender and smoking: do women really find it harder to give up?' *British Journal of Addiction*, 79: 57–61.

11. Waldron I (1991) 'Patterns and causes of gender differences in smoking', *Social Science and Medicine*, 32, 9: 989–1005.

12. Marsh A and Matheson J (1983) *Smoking Attitudes and Behaviour*, London: HMSO.

13. Lader D and Matheson J (1991) *Smoking Among Secondary School Children in 1990*, London: HMSO.

14. US Department of Health and Human Services (1988) *The Health Consequences of Cigarettes: Nicotine Addiction*, Atlanta: Atlanta Centre for Disease Control, Centre for Health Promotion and Education, Office on Smoking and Health.

15. Warburton D M, Revell A and Walters A C (1988) 'Nicotine as a resource' in Rand M and Thuran K (eds) *The Pharmacology of Nicotine*, London: IRL Press.

16. Royal College of Physicians of London (1992), *Smoking and the Young*, London: Royal College of Physicians of London.

17. Department of Health and Social Services (Northern Ireland) (1986) *Smoking Among Secondary School Children*, Belfast: DHSS (NI).

18. Swan A V, Melia R J W, Fitzsimons B, Breeze E and Murray M (1989) 'Why do more girls than boys smoke cigarettes?' *Health Education Journal*, 48: 59–64.

19. Balding J (1987) *Young People in 1986*, London: HMSO.

20. Gillies P (1988) 'Health behaviour and health promotion in youth' in Martin C and McQueen D V (eds) *The New Public Health*, Edinburgh: Edinburgh University Press.

21. Aaro L E, Wold B, Kannas L and Rimpela M (1986) 'Health behaviour in school children: a WHO cross-national survey', *Health Promotion*, 1, 1: 17–33.

22. Goddard E (1990) *Why Children Start Smoking*, London: HMSO.

23. Oakley A, Brannen J and Dodd K (1992) 'Young people, gender and smoking in the United Kingdom', *Health Promotion International*, 7, 2: 75–88.

24. Charlton A and Blair V (1989) 'Predicting the onset of smoking in boys and girls', *Social Science and Medicine*, 29, 7: 813–18.

25. Charlton A (1984) 'Smoking and weight control in teenagers', *Public Health, London*, 98: 277–81.

26. Prichard C, Cotton A and Cox M (1992) 'Truancy and illegal drug use, and knowledge of HIV infection in 932 14–16 year old adolescents', *Journal of Adolescence*, 15: 1–17.

27. Townsend J, Wilkes H and Jarvis M (1991) 'Adolescent smokers seen in general practice: health, lifestyle, physical measurements and response to anti-smoking advice', *British Medical Journal*, 303: 947–50.

28. Measham F, Newcombe R and Parker H (1993) *An Investigation into the Relationship between Drinking and Deviant Behaviour Among Young People*, Manchester: Department of Social Policy and Social Work, University of Manchester.

29. Fidler W, MacLell, L, Raab G and Charlton A (1992) 'Smoking: a special need?' *British Journal of Addiction*, 87: 1583–91.

30. Green G, MacIntyre S, West P and Erob R (1990) 'Do children of lone parents smoke more because their mothers do?' *British Journal of Addiction*, 85: 1497–1500.

31. Piepe T, Cattermole B, Charlton P, Morley R, Morey J and Yervell P (1988) 'Girls' smoking and self-esteem – the adolescent context', *Health Education Journal*, 47: 83–5.

32. Graham H (1987) 'Women's smoking and family health', *Social Science and Medicine*, 25: 47–56.

33. Lawson E (1993) *The Role of Smoking in the Lives of Low-income Pregnant Adolescents*, Kentucky: Department of Behavioral Science, University of Kentucky.

Chapter 3

1. Marmot M (1984) *Immigrant Mortality in England and Wales. 1970–78*, London: HMSO.

2. Graham, H (1988) 'Women and smoking in the United Kingdom: the implications for health promotion', *Health Promotion*, 3, 4: 371–82.

3. Ahmad W I U, Kernohan E E M and Baker M R (1988) 'Alcohol and cigarette consumption among white and Asian general practice patients', *Health Education Journal*, 47, 4: 128–9.

4. Bhopal B S (1986) 'Asians' knowledge and behaviour on preventive health issues: smoking, alcohol, heart disease, pregnancy, rickets, malaria prophylaxis and surma', *Community Medicine*, 8, 4: 315–21.

5. Cox B D (ed) (1987) *Health and Lifestyle Survey*, London: Health Promotion Research Trust.

6. Howlett B C, Ahmad W I U and Murray R (1992) 'An exploration of white, Asian and Afro-Caribbean peoples' concepts of health and illness causation', *New Community*, 18, 2: 281–92.

7. Oakley A, Brannen J and Dodd K (1992) 'Young people, gender and smoking in the United Kingdom', *Health Promotion International*, 7, 2: 75–88.

8. Stevens A (1987) *Evaluation of a Satellite Antenatal Clinic Interim Report*, Birmingham: Birmingham Maternity Hospital.

9. Drury B (1991) 'Sikh girls and the maintenance of an ethnic culture', *New Community*, 17, 3: 387–99.

10. Eyles J and Donovan J (1990) *The Social Effects of Health Policy*, Aldershot: Avebury.

11. Cooper R and Simmons B E (1985) 'Cigarette smoking and ill health among Black Americans', *New York State Journal of Medicine*, July: 344–49.

12. Fiore M C, Novotny T E, Pierce J P, Hatziandreu E J, Patel K M and Davis R M (1989) 'Trends in cigarette smoking in the United States', *JAMA*, 261, 1: 49–55.

13. Hay D R (1984) 'Intercensal trends in cigarette smoking in New Zealand I: age, sex and ethnic status', *The New Zealand Medical Journal*, 97, 755: 283–5.

14. Ritchie J (1990) 'Women and smoking: a lethal deception', *Women's Studies International Forum*, 13, 3: 201–8.

15. Wald N, Kiryluk S, Darby S, Doll R, Pike M and Peto R (1988) *UK Smoking Statistics*, Oxford: Oxford University Press.

16. Office of Population Censuses and Surveys (1992) *General Household Survey 1990*, London: HMSO.

17. Madeley R J, Gillies P A, Power, F L and Symonds E M (1989) 'Nottingham Mothers Stop Smoking Project – baseline survey of smoking in pregnancy', *Community Medicine*, 11, 2: 124–30.

18. Waterson E J and Murray-Lyon I M (1989) 'Drinking and smoking patterns amongst women attending an antenatal clinic – II during pregnancy', *Alcohol and Alcoholism*, 24, 2: 163–73.

19. White A, Freeth S and O'Brien M (1992) *Infant Feeding 1990*, London: HMSO.

20. Barker, M E, McClean S I, McKenna P G, Reid N G, Strain J J, Thompson K A, Williamson A P and Wright M E (1989) *Diet, Lifestyle and Health in Northern Ireland*, Coleraine: Centre for Applied Health Studies, University of Ulster.

21. Economic Research Unit (1993) *Smoking and Pregnancy: Survey of General Practitioners*, London: Economic Research Unit.

22. Hunt S M, Martin C J, Platt S, Lewis C and Morris G (1988) *Damp Housing, Mould Growth and Health Status*, Edinburgh: Research Unit in Health and Behavioural Change, University of Edinburgh.

23. Pierce J P (1989) 'International comparisons of trends in cigarette smoking prevalence', *American Journal of Public Health*, 79, 2: 152–57.

24. Pierce J P (1987) 'Uptake and quitting smoking trends in Australia, 1974-1984', *Organisation*, 64: 447–56.

25. Chollat-Traquet C (1992) *Women and Tobacco*, Geneva: WHO.

26. Oakley A (1989) 'Smoking in pregnancy: smokescreen or risk factor? Towards a materialist analysis', *Sociology of Health and Illness*, 11, 4: 311–335.

27. Simms M and Smith C (1986) *Teenage Mothers and Their Partners*, London: HMSO.

28. Dowsett S J (1985) 'Smoking attitudes and habits during pregnancy: Sheffield 1983', *Health Education Journal*, 44: 83–6.

29. McKnight A and Merrett J D (1986) 'Smoking in pregnancy – a health education problem', *Journal of the Royal College of General Pratitioners*, 36: 161–4.

30. Bradshaw J and Millar J (1991) *Lone Parent Families in the UK*, London: HMSO.

31. Thomas A and Niner P (1989) *Living in Temporary Accommodation: A Study of Homeless People*, London: HMSO.

32. Graham H (1976) 'Smoking in pregnancy: the attitudes of expectant mothers', *Social Science and Medicine*, 10: 399–405.

33. Graham, H (1987) 'Women's smoking and family health', *Social Science and Medicine*, 25,1: 47–56.

34. Gillies P A, Madeley R J and Power F L (1989) 'Why do pregnant women smoke?' *Community Medicine*, 103: 337–43.

35. Lawson E (1993) *The Role of Smoking in the Lives of Low-income Pregnant Adolescents*, Kentucky: Department of Behavioral Science, University of Kentucky.

36. Office of Population Censuses and Surveys (1977) *Smoking and Professional People*, London: Department of Health and Social Security.

37. Spencer J K (1984) 'Nurses' cigarette smoking in England and Wales', *International Journal of Nursing Studies*, 221, 2: 69–79.

38. Elkind A K (1988) 'Smoking and the female professions: pre-occupational influences on the behaviour of recruits to nursing and teaching', *Social Science and Medicine*, 26, 2: 243–51.

39. Haverty S, MacLeod Clark J and Kendall S (1986) 'Nurses and smoking education: a literature review', *Nurse Education Today*, 6: 237–43.

40. Gubbay J (1992) *Smoking and the Workplace*, Norwich: Centre for Health Policy Research, University of East Anglia.

41. Wells J (1987) *Women and Smoking: an Evaluation of the Role of Stress in Smoking Cessation and Relapse*, Southampton: Department of Psychology, University of Southampton.

42. Nicotinell (1993) *Smoking Mothers with Young Children: The Hidden Dilemma*, London: Nicotinell.

43. Davies J and Evans F (1991) 'The Newcastle Community Midwifery Care Project' in Robinson S and Thomson A (eds) *Midwives, Research and Childbirth*, Volume 2, London: Chapman and Hall.

Chapter 4

1. Stanworth, M (1984) 'Women and class analysis: a reply to John Goldthorpe', *Sociology*, 18, 2: 159–70.

2. Pugh, H and Moser, K (1990) 'Measuring women's mortality differences' in Roberts, H (ed) *Women's Health Counts*, London: Routledge.

3. Arber, S (1990) 'Revealing women's health: re-analysing the General Household Survey' in Roberts, H (ed) *Women's Health Counts*, London: Routledge.

4. Blaxter, M (1990) *Health and Lifestyles*, London: Routledge.

5. Goldblatt, P (1990) *Longitudinal Study: Mortality and Social Organisation*, LS No. 6, London: OPCS.

6. Goldberg, D and Williams, P (1988) *A User's Guide to the General Health Questionnaire*, London: NFER – Nelson.

7. Tennant, C (1977) 'The General Health Questionnaire: a valid index of psychological impairment in Australian populations', *Medical Journal of Australia*, ii, 12: 392–4.

8. Banks M H (1983) 'Validation of the General Health Questionnaire in a young community sample', *Psychological Medicine*, 13: 249–54.

9. Tarnopolsky, A, Hand D J, McLean, E K, Roberts, H and Wiggins, R D, (1979) 'Validity and uses of a screening questionnaire (GHQ) in the community', *British Journal of Psychiatry*, 134: 508–15.

10. Kozlowski L T and Heatherton T F (1990) 'Self-report issues in cigarette smoking: state of the art and future directions', *Behavioural Assessment*, 12: 53–75.

11. Huppert F A and Weinstein Garcia A (1991) 'Qualitative differences in psychiatric symptoms between high risk groups assessed on a screening test (GHQ-30), *Social Psychiatry and Psychiatric Epidemiology*, 26: 252–58.

12. McKennell A and Thomas R (1967) *Adults' and Adolescents' Smoking Habits and Attitudes*, London: HMSO.

13. Marsh A and Matheson J (1983) *Smoking Attitudes and Behaviour*, London: HMSO.

14. Cox B D (ed) (1987) *The Health and Lifestyle Survey*, London: Health Promotion Research Trust.

15. Ben-Shlomo Y, Sheiham A and Marmot M (1991) 'Smoking and health' in Jowell R, Brook L and Taylor B (eds) *British Social Attitudes: the 8th Report*, Aldershot: Dartmouth.

Chapter 5

1. Office of Population Censuses and Surveys (1992) *General Household Survey 1990*, London: HMSO.

2. Dowsett S J (1985) 'Smoking attitudes and habits during pregnancy; Sheffield 1983', *Health Education Journal*, 44: 83–6.

3. McKnight A and Merrett J D (1986) 'Smoking in pregnancy – a health education problem', *Journal of the Royal College of General Practitioners*, 36: 161–64.

4. Gillies P A, Madeley R J and Power F L (1989) 'Why do pregnant women smoke?' *Community Medicine*, 103: 337–43.

5. Marsh A and Matheson J (1983) *Smoking Attitudes and Behaviour*, London: HMSO.

6. Blaxter M (1990) *Health and Lifestyles*, London: Routledge.

7. McKnight A and Marrett J D (1986) 'Smoking in pregnancy – a health education problem', *Journal of the Royal College of General Practitioners*, 36: 161–64.

8. Graham H (1976) 'Smoking in pregnancy: the attitudes of expectant mothers', *Social Science and Medicine*, 10: 399–405.

9. Graham H (1987) 'Women's smoking and family health', *Social Science and Medicine*, 25, 1: 47–56.

10. Oakley A (1989) 'Smoking in pregnancy: smokescreen or risk factor? Towards a materialist analysis', *Sociology of Health and Illness*, 11, 4: 311–335.

11. Simms M and Smith C (1986) *Teenage Mothers and Their Partners*, London: HMSO.

12. Madeley R K, Gillies P A, Power F L and Symonds E M (1989) 'Nottingham Mothers Stop Smoking Project – baseline survey of smoking in pregnancy', *Community Medicine*, 11, 2: 124–30.

13. Waterson E J and Murray-Lyon I M (1989) 'Drinking and smoking patterns amongst women attending an ante-natal clinic – 1 before pregnancy, *Alcohol and Alcoholism*, 24, 2: 153–62.

14. White A, Freeth S and O'Brien M (1992) *Infant Feeding 1990*, London: HMSO.

15. Shiffman S (1982) 'Relapse following smoking cessation: a situation analysis', *Journal of Consulting and Clinical Psychology*, 50: 71–86.

16. Cnattingius S, Landmark G and Meirik O (1992) 'Who continues to smoke while pregnant?', *Journal of Epidemiology and Community Health*, 46: 218–21.

17. Lindqvist R and Aberg H (1992) 'Smoking habits before, during and after pregnancy among Swedish women and their partners in suburban Stockholm', *Scandinavian Journal of Primary Health Care*, 10: 12–15.

18. Fingerhut L A, Kleinman J C and Kennedy K S (1990) 'Smoking before, during and after pregnancy', *American Journal of Public Health*, 80: 541–44.

19. Wakefield M, Gillies P, Graham H, Madeley R and Symonds M (1993) 'Characteristics associated with smoking cessation during pregnancy among working class women', *British Journal of Addiction*, forthcoming.

20. Quinn V P, Mullen P D and Ershoff D H (1991) 'Women who stop smoking spontaneously prior to prenatal care and predictors of relapse before delivery', *Addictive Behaviours*, 16: 29–40.

Chapter 6

1. Pearson M, Dawson C, Moore H and Spencer S (1993) 'Health on borrowed time? Prioritising and meeting needs in low-income households', *Health and Social Care*, 1: 45–54.

2. Moser K A, Pugh H S and Goldblatt P O (1988) 'Inequalities in health: looking at mortality differentials using an alternative approach', *British Medical Journal*, 296: 1221–4.

3. Pugh H, Power C, Goldblatt P and Arber S (1991) 'Women's lung cancer mortality, socio-economic status and changing smoking patterns', *Social Science and Medicine*, 32, 10: 1005–10.

4. Department of Environment (1983) *Urban Deprivation*, Inner Cities Directorate, London: Department of Environment.

Chapter 7

1. Carmody T P, Brischetto C S, Matarazzo J D, O'Donnell R P and Connor W E (1985) 'Co-current use of cigarettes, alcohol and coffee in healthy community living men and women', *Health Psychology*, 4, 4: 323–35.

2. White A, Freeth S and O'Brien M (1992) *Infant Feeding 1990*, London: HMSO.

3. Waterson E J and Lyon I M (1989) 'Drinking and smoking patterns amongst women attending antenatal clinic – I. Before pregnancy', *Alcohol and Alcoholism*, 24, 2: 153–62.

4. Waterson E J and Lyon I M (1989) 'Drinking and smoking patterns amongst women attending antenatal clinic – II. During pregnancy', *Alcohol and Alcoholism*, 24, 2: 163–73.

5. Perkins K A (1992) 'Effects of tobacco on calorie intake', *British Journal of Addiction*, 87: 193–205.

6. Perkins K A, Denier C A, Mayer J A, Scott R R and Dubbert P M (1987) 'Weight gain associated with reductions in smoking rate and nicotine content', *International Journal of the Addictions*, 22: 575–81.

7. Charlton A (1984) 'Smoking and weight control in teenagers', *Public Health. London*, 98: 277–81.

8. Oakley A, Brannen J and Dodd K (1992) 'Young people, gender and smoking in the United Kingdom', *Health Promotion International*, 7, 2: 75–88.

Chapter 8

1. Office of Population Censuses and Surveys (1992) *General Household Survey 1990*, London: HMSO.

2. Royal College of General Practitioners (1981) *Health and Prevention in Primary Care*, Report from General Practice 18, London: Royal College of General Pratitioners.

3. Health Education Council (1985) *Smokestop National Conference Proceedings*, London: Health Education Council and University of Southampton.

4. MacLeod Clark J, Haverty S and Kendall S (1987) *Helping Patients and Clients to Stop Smoking: Assessing the Effectiveness of the Nurse's Role*, Research Report No. 19, London: Health Education Council.

5. MacLeod Clark J and Haverty J (1992) *Smoking Cessation: the Health Professional's Role*, London: Health Education Authority.

6. Ben-Shlomo B, Sheiham A and Marmot M (1991) 'Smoking and health' in Jowell R, Brook L and Taylor (eds) *British Social Attitudes: the 8th Report*, Aldershot: Dartmouth.

7. McKennell A and Thomas R (1967) *Adults' and Adolescents' Smoking Habits and Attitudes*, London: HMSO.

8. Marsh A and Matheson J (1983) *Smoking Attitudes and Behaviour*, London: HMSO.

9. Blaxter M (1990) *Health and Lifestyles*, London: Routledge.

10. Madeley R J, Gillies P A, Power F L and Symonds E M (1989) 'Nottingham Mothers Stop Smoking Project – baseline survey of smoking in pregnancy', *Community Medicine*, 11, 2: 124–30.

11. Hunt S and Martin C (1988) 'Health-related behavioural change – a test of a new model' *Psychology and Health*, 2: 209–30.

12. Davies J and Evans F (1991) 'The Newcastle Community Midwifery Care Project' in Robinson S and Thompson A (eds) *Midwives, Research and Childbirth*, Volume 2, London: Chapman and Hall.

13. Sutton S, Marsh A and Matheson J (1990) 'Microanalysis of smokers' beliefs about the consequences of quitting: results from a large population sample', *Journal of Applied Social Psychology*, 20, 22: 1847–62.

14. Hunt S M and MacLeod M (1987) 'Health and behavioural change: some lay perspectives', *Community Medicine*, 9: 68–76.

15. Stott C H and Pill R M (1990) *Making Changes: A Study of Working Class Mothers and the Changes Made in Their Health-related Behaviour Over 5 years*, Cardiff: Department of General Practice, University of Wales College of Medicine.

16. Blackburn C and Graham H (1992) *Smoking Among Working Class Mothers: Information Pack*, Coventry: Department of Applied Social Studies, University of Warwick.

17. Graham H (1993) 'Smoking among working class mothers', *Primary Health Care*, 3, 2: 15–16.

18. Blackburn C (1993) 'Gender, class and smoking cessation work', *Health Visitor*, 66, 3: 83–5.

Printed in the United Kingdom for HMSO.
Dd.296446, 12/93, C15, 3396/4, 5673, 263095.